Design: Jill Coote
Recipe Photography: Peter Barry
Recipe styling: Jacqueline Bellefontaine, Siân Davies,
Bridgeen Deery and Wendy Devenish
Jacket and Illustration Artwork: Jane Winton,
courtesy of Bernard Thornton Artists, London
Editorial: Laura Potts

CLB 3355
Published by Grange Books,
an imprint of Grange Books Limited,
The Grange, Grange Yard, London.
© 1993 CLB Publishing,
Godalming, Surrey, England.
All rights reserved.
Printed and bound in Singapore
Published 1993
ISBN 1-85627-314-8

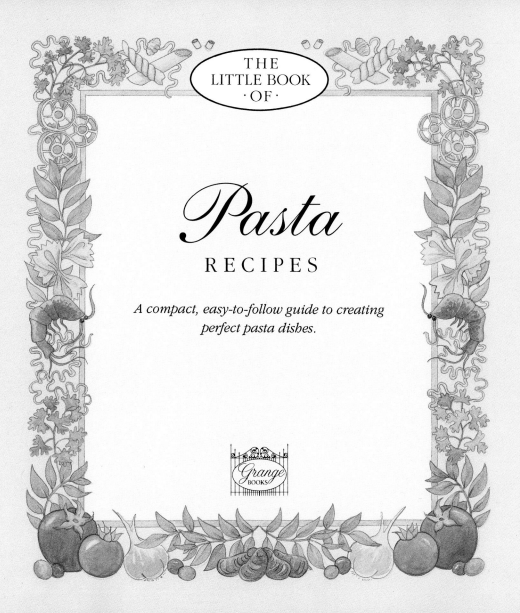

THE LITTLE BOOK ·OF·

Pasta

RECIPES

A compact, easy-to-follow guide to creating
perfect pasta dishes.

Grange
BOOKS

Introduction

*T*he basic recipe for pasta – which at its most simple is literally a *paste* made from flour and water – appears in many cuisines, and takes many forms. It is, however, particularly associated with the Italian and Chinese culinary traditions. The debate as to which of these nations should be credited with its invention has been hotly argued. One thing, however, is certain. Though not unique to Italian cooking, pasta has to a certain extent become synonymous with it.

Pasta comes in a bewildering variety of shapes and sizes. The fundamental reason for this profusion does not lie, as many would believe, in Italian extravagance, or in rivalry between competing dried pasta manufacturers. In fact, different varieties of pasta absorb different amounts of sauce, with some shapes of pasta complementing some sauces better than others. For example, long varieties of dried pasta are best served with oil-based sauces, and generally speaking do not combine well with meat sauces. Rich, creamy sauces and meat sauces, on the other hand, go well with short-cut varieties of pasta, especially those which are hollow, or have grooves where the sauce can be trapped.

Most supermarkets now stock a wide variety of fresh, as well as dried pasta. Many people prefer dried pasta, for the simple reason that they are more familiar with it and know exactly how to cook it. Like dried pasta, fresh pasta is cooked in boiling salted water, with a little oil to stop it sticking together. Cooking times for fresh and

dried pasta vary, with dried pasta taking slightly longer. It is essential that pasta is not over-cooked, as there is nothing less appetizing than a plateful of limp, soggy spaghetti or tagliatelle. Pasta should be cooked until it is *al dente*, which means tender but firm. There are many ways to test whether pasta is cooked, but the best way is to take a piece and taste it.

Pasta sauces do not have to be elaborate. In fact some of tastiest, most-loved sauces can be prepared very quickly. Melted butter, black pepper and the lightest sprinkling of freshly grated Parmesan cheese, for example, or the classic *carbonara* sauce with cream, eggs and bacon make delicious easy sauces. The essence of a good pasta sauce lies in the use of fresh ingredients, whose flavours enhance each other. Ripe tomatoes, fragrant herbs, black olives and juicy, sweet peppers, are commonly found in pasta sauces.

This book is an invaluable companion to the experienced and inexperienced cook alike. The selection of recipes reflects the versatility of pasta, offering a range of recipes, from those that can be put together very quickly, such as *Tagliatelle with Garlic and Oil*, to the more elaborate baked dishes such as *Lasagne* and *Cannelloni*. The step-by-step instructions explain how to create a variety of perfect pasta dishes, highlighting the skills needed to make fresh pasta, and giving ideas for different fillings and sauces.

Minestra

SERVES 4-6

A wholesome soup which makes an ideal starter.

PREPARATION: 15 mins
COOKING: 45 mins

115g/4oz short-cut macaroni
30ml/2 tbsps olive oil
1 onion
1 carrot
1 stick celery
1½ litres/3 pints water
225g/8oz fresh spinach
2 tomatoes
1 tsp rosemary
2 tbsps chopped parsley
2 cloves garlic, crushed
60g/2oz Parmesan cheese, grated
Salt and pepper

Step 4 Add the shredded spinach leaves to the soup.

1. Cut onion, carrot and celery into thick matchstick strips.

2. Heat oil in a large, heavy pan, and fry vegetable strips until just browning, stirring occasionally.

3. Pour on water, add salt and pepper, and let simmer for 20 minutes.

4. Meanwhile, wash and cut spinach leaves into shreds, add to soup and cook for 10 minutes.

5. Scald and skin tomatoes, and chop roughly, removing seeds.

6. Add tomatoes, macaroni, garlic, parsley and rosemary to the soup, and simmer for a further 10 minutes.

7. Adjust seasoning. Serve with grated Parmesan cheese if desired.

Step 1 Cut onion, carrot and celery into thick matchstick strips.

Tagliatelle Carbonara

SERVES 4

Bacon, cream and eggs combine to make a rich pasta sauce.

PREPARATION: 10 mins
COOKING: 15 mins

300g/10oz tagliatelle
30g/1oz butter or margarine
120g/4oz streaky bacon rashers, chopped
1 tbsp olive oil
4 tbsps single cream
Pinch of paprika
60g/2oz Parmesan cheese, grated
2 eggs
Salt and pepper

Step 7 Add bacon mixture and egg mixture, and toss together.

1. Heat the oil in a frying pan, and cook the bacon over a moderate heat until just browning.

2. Add the paprika and cook for 1 minute.

3. Add the cream, and stir.

4. Beat together the eggs and grated cheese.

5. Cook the tagliatelle in lots of boiling salted water for 10 minutes, or until tender but still firm.

6. Drain the pasta, return to pan with butter and black pepper, and toss.

7. Add bacon mixture and egg mixture, and toss together. Add salt to taste. Serve immediately.

Step 4 Beat together eggs and grated cheese.

Spaghetti with Tomato, Salami and Green Olives

SERVES 4

This robust pasta dish is ideal for a quick supper or light lunch.

PREPARATION: 15 mins
COOKING: 15 mins

300g/10oz spaghetti
400g/14oz tin plum tomatoes
150g/5oz salami, sliced
200g/7oz green olives, stoned and chopped
1 clove garlic, crushed
2 tbsps olive oil
½ tbsp oregano
60g/2oz pecorino cheese, grated
Salt and pepper

Step 2 Add oregano, salami and olives and heat gently.

Step 1 Purée tomatoes and push through a sieve into a saucepan.

1. Purée tomatoes, and push through a sieve into a saucepan.

2. Add oregano, salami and olives, and heat gently.

3. Add salt and pepper to taste.

4. Meanwhile, cook spaghetti in plenty of boiling salted water for 10 minutes. Drain well.

5. Heat olive oil, garlic and freshly-ground black pepper in the pan used to cook the spaghetti.

6. Add spaghetti, and pour the sauce over. Toss well and serve immediately with pecorino cheese.

Pasta with Fresh Tomato and Basil Sauce

SERVES 4

Fresh tomato and basil make a classic sauce for pasta.

PREPARATION: 15-20 mins
COOKING: 10-15 mins

---

1 small onion, finely chopped
450g/1lb fresh tomatoes
2 tbsps tomato purée
1 orange
2 cloves garlic, crushed
Salt and freshly ground black pepper
140ml/¼ pint red wine
140ml/¼ pint chicken stock
2 tbsps coarsely chopped basil
340g/12oz wholemeal pasta

---

1. Peel and finely chop the onion.

2. Cut a small cross in the skins of the tomatoes and plunge them into boiling water for 30 seconds. Remove and carefully peel away the loosened skin.

3. Cut the tomatoes into quarters, and remove and discard the pips. Chop the tomato flesh roughly, and put this, the onion and the tomato purée into a large saucepan.

4. Heat the onion and tomatoes over a gentle heat, stirring continuously until the tomatoes soften and begin to lose their juice.

Step 1 To chop an onion finely, pierce the peeled onion with a fork and use this to hold the vegetable steady whilst you chop.

5. Finely grate the rind from the orange. Cut the orange in half and squeeze out the juice.

6. Put the orange rind and juice into a large saucepan along with all the remaining ingredients, and bring to the boil.

7. Continue to boil until the sauce has reduced and thickened and the vegetables are soft.

8. Whilst the sauce is cooking, put the pasta into another saucepan with enough boiling water to cover. Season with a little salt and cook for 10-15 minutes, or until the pasta is soft.

9. Drain the pasta in a colander, and stir it into the hot sauce. Serve at once with a salad.

Tagliatelle with Garlic and Oil

SERVES 4

Garlic and oil combine to make the simplest of pasta sauces.

PREPARATION: 5 mins
COOKING: 10 mins

300g/10oz green tagliatelle
150ml/¼ pint olive oil
3 cloves garlic, crushed
2 tbsps chopped parsley
Salt and pepper

Step 5 Toss the tagliatelle in the sauce to coat well.

Step 5 Add sauce to tagliatelle.

1. Cook the tagliatelle in lots of boiling salted water for 10 minutes, or until tender but still firm, stirring occasionally.

2. Meanwhile, heat the oil in a pan and, when warm, add peeled, crushed garlic.

3. Fry gently until golden brown.

4. Add chopped parsley, and salt and pepper to taste.

5. Drain tagliatelle. Add sauce, and toss to coat well. Serve hot.

Home-made Tagliatelle with Summer Sauce

SERVES 4

Home-made pasta is in a class by itself.

PREPARATION: 30 mins
COOKING: 5-6 mins

Pasta Dough
120g/4oz plain flour
120g/4oz fine semolina
2 large eggs
2 tsps olive oil
Pinch salt

Sauce
450g/1lb unpeeled tomatoes, seeded and cut
 into small dice
1 large green pepper, cored, seeded and cut in
 small dice
1 onion, cut in small dice
1 tbsp chopped fresh basil
1 tbsp chopped fresh parsley
2 cloves garlic, crushed
140ml/¼ pint olive oil and vegetable oil mixed

1. Place the flours in a mound on a work
surface and make a well in the centre. Place the
eggs, oil and salt in the centre of the well.

2. Using a fork, beat the ingredients in the
centre to blend them and gradually incorporate
the flour from the outside edge.

3. When half the flour is incorporated, start
kneading using the palms of the hands and not

Step 4 Roll the
dough out
thinly and cut
into thin strips.

the fingers. Cover the dough and leave it to rest
for 15 minutes.

4. Divide the dough in quarters and roll out
thinly with a rolling pin on a floured surface or
use a pasta machine, dusting dough lightly with
flour before rolling. Allow the sheets of pasta to
dry for about 10 minutes on a floured surface.
Cut the sheets into strips about 5mm/¼ inch
wide by hand or machine, dusting lightly with
flour while cutting. Leave the cut pasta to dry
while preparing the sauce.

5. Combine all the sauce ingredients, mixing
well. Cover and refrigerate.

6. Cook the pasta for 5-6 minutes in boiling
salted water with a spoonful of oil. Drain the
pasta and rinse under very hot water. Toss in a
colander to drain excess water. Place in a
serving dish and pour the cold sauce over.

Penne with Ham and Asparagus

SERVES 4

The Italian word penne means quills, due to the diagonal cut on both ends.

Preparation: 20 mins
Cooking: 10 mins

225g/8oz penne
340g/12oz fresh asparagus
120g/4oz cooked ham
30g/2 tbsps butter or margarine
280ml/½ pint double cream

1. Using a swivel vegetable peeler, scrape the sides of the asparagus spears starting about 5cm/2 inches from the top. Cut off the ends of the spears about 2.5cm/1 inch from the bottom.

2. Cut the ham into strips about 1.25cm/½ inch thick.

3. Bring a sauté pan of salted water to the boil. Move the pan so it is half on and half off direct

Step 1 Peel the asparagus stalks with a swivel vegetable peeler.

Step 4 Cut ham and cooked asparagus into 2.5cm/1 inch lengths. Leave the asparagus tips whole.

heat. Place in the asparagus spears so that the tips are off the heat. Cover and bring back to the boil. Cook the asparagus spears for about 2 minutes. Drain and allow to cool.

4. Cut the asparagus into 5cm/1 inch lengths, leaving the tips whole.

5. Melt the butter in the sauté pan and add the asparagus and ham. Cook briefly to evaporate the liquid, and add the cream. Bring to the boil and cook for about 5 minutes to thicken the cream.

6. Meanwhile, cook the pasta in boiling salted water with a little oil for about 10-12 minutes.

7. Drain the pasta and rinse under hot water. Toss in a colander to drain and mix with the sauce. Serve with grated Parmesan cheese, if desired.

Spaghetti Amatriciana

SERVES 4

Chilli pepper brings a fiery taste to this pasta sauce.

PREPARATION: 20-25 mins
COOKING: 10-12 mins

1 onion
6 strips smoked bacon
450g/1lb ripe tomatoes
1 red chilli pepper
1½ tbsps oil
340g/12oz spaghetti

1. Slice the onion thinly. Remove rind from the bacon and cut into thin strips.

2. Drop the tomatoes into boiling water for 6-8 seconds. Remove and place in cold water, and leave to cool. This will make the peels easier to remove.

3. When the tomatoes are peeled, cut them in half and remove the seeds and pulp with a

Step 2 Placing tomatoes in boiling water and then in cold water makes the skins easier to remove.

Step 4 Remove the stems, seeds and cores from the chilli pepper, cut into thin strips and then chop into fine dice.

teaspoon. Chop the tomato flesh roughly and set it aside.

4. Cut the chilli pepper in half lengthways. Remove the seeds and core and cut the pepper into thin strips. Cut the strips into small dice.

5. Heat the oil in a sauté pan and add the onion and bacon. Stir over medium heat for about 5 minutes, until the onion is transparent. Drain off excess fat and add the tomatoes and chilli and mix well. Simmer the sauce gently, uncovered, for about 5 minutes, stirring occasionally.

6. Meanwhile, cook the spaghetti in boiling salted water with a little oil for about 10-12 minutes. Drain and rinse in hot water and toss in a colander to dry. To serve, spoon the sauce on top of the spaghetti and sprinkle with freshly grated Parmesan cheese.

Spirali with Spinach and Bacon

SERVES 4

Pasta doesn't have to have a sauce that cooks for hours.
This whole dish takes about 20 minutes. True Italian "fast food"!

PREPARATION: 10 mins
COOKING: 10 mins

340g/12oz pasta spirals
225g/8oz fresh spinach
90g/3oz bacon
1 clove garlic, crushed
1 small red or green chilli pepper
1 small red sweet pepper
1 small onion
3 tbsps olive oil
Salt and pepper

1. Cook the pasta in boiling salted water for about 10-12 minutes or until just tender. Drain in a colander and rinse. Keep the pasta in a bowl of water until ready to use.

Step 2 Tear stalks off the spinach and wash the leaves well.

Step 4 Roll up the leaves in several layers to shred them faster.

2. Tear the stalks off the spinach and wash the leaves well, changing the water several times. Set aside to drain.

3. Remove the rind from the bacon and dice the bacon finely. Cut the chilli and the red pepper in half, remove the stems, core and seeds and slice finely. Slice the onion thinly.

4. Shred the spinach finely.

5. Heat the oil in a sauté pan and add garlic, onion, peppers and bacon. Fry for 2 minutes, add the spinach and fry for a further 2 minutes, stirring continuously. Season with salt and pepper.

6. Drain the pasta spirals and toss them in a colander to remove excess water. Mix with the spinach sauce and serve immediately.

Gianfottere Salad

SERVES 4

This delicious Italian salad makes the most of summer vegetables.

PREPARATION: 30 mins
COOKING: 30 mins

---

1 small aubergine
2 tomatoes
1 large courgette
1 red pepper
1 green pepper
1 medium onion
1 clove garlic, peeled
4 tbsps olive oil
Salt and pepper
450g/1lb wholemeal pasta spirals

---

1. Cut the aubergine into 1cm/½-inch slices. Sprinkle with salt and leave for 30 minutes.

2. Chop the tomatoes roughly and remove the cores.

3. Cut the courgette into 1cm/½-inch slices.

Step 1 Cut the aubergine into 1cm/½-inch slices and sprinkle with plenty of salt.

Step 8 Add the aubergine, courgette, peppers, tomatoes and garlic to the onion in the frying pan.

4. Core and seed the peppers, and chop them roughly.

5. Chop the onion. Crush the garlic.

6. Heat 3 tbsps olive oil in a frying pan, and fry the onion gently, until it is transparent.

7. Rinse the salt from the aubergine and pat dry. Chop the aubergine roughly.

8. Stir the aubergine, courgette, peppers, tomatoes and garlic into the onion, and fry gently for 20 minutes. Season to taste, and allow to cool completely.

9. Cook the pasta spirals in plenty of boiling salted water for 10-15 minutes.

10. Rinse the pasta in cold water and drain well.

11. Put the pasta into a large mixing bowl, and stir in the remaining olive oil.

12. Stir in the vegetables, mixing well.

Tuna and Tomato Salad

SERVES 4

Serve this salad as part of a summer lunch with a green salad and French bread.

PREPARATION: 10 mins
COOKING: 15 mins

1 tbsp chopped fresh basil, or marjoram
6 tbsps French dressing
340g/12oz pasta spirals
6 tomatoes
340g/12oz tinned tuna fish, drained

1. Mix the basil or marjoram, with the French dressing.

2. Cook the pasta in a large saucepan of boiling, lightly salted water, for about 10 minutes.

3. Rinse in cold water and drain well, shaking off any excess water.

4. Put the pasta into a large bowl and toss with

Step 4 Mix the pasta spirals with 3 tbsps of the French dressing in a large bowl.

Step 7 Add the tuna to the pasta and mix together gently.

3 tablespoons of the French dressing, mixing well to ensure that they are evenly coated. Leave to cool.

5. Slice enough of the tomatoes to arrange around the outside of the serving dish and then chop the rest.

6. Put the chopped tomatoes into another bowl and pour over the remaining French dressing. Put this into the centre of a serving dish.

7. Add the flaked tuna to the pasta and toss together gently.

8. Pile the pasta and tuna over the chopped tomatoes in the centre of the dish.

9. Arrange the tomato slices around the edge of the serving dish and chill well until required.

Mushroom Pasta Salad

SERVES 4

The piquant lemon marinade brings zest to this easy salad.

PREPARATION: 10 mins, plus 1 hr to marinate the
    mushrooms
COOKING: 15 mins

---

5 tbsps olive oil
Juice of 2 lemons
1 tsp fresh chopped basil
1 tsp fresh chopped parsley
Salt and pepper
225g/8oz mushrooms
225g/8oz wholemeal pasta shapes

---

1. Mix together the olive oil, lemon juice, herbs and seasoning.

Step 2 Use a sharp knife to slice the mushrooms thinly.

Step 6 Stir the cooled pasta into the marinated mushrooms, mixing well to coat evenly.

2. Finely slice the mushrooms and add these to the lemon dressing in the bowl, stirring well.

3. Cover the bowl and allow to stand in a cool place for at least 1 hour.

4. Cook the pasta in boiling, salted water for 10-15 minutes.

5. Rinse the pasta in cold water and drain well.

6. Add the pasta to the marinated mushrooms and lemon dressing, mixing well to coat evenly.

7. Adjust the seasoning if necessary, then chill well before serving.

Macaroni Cheese with Frankfurters

SERVES 4

A hearty family supper dish, ideal for cold winter evenings.

PREPARATION: 10 mins
COOKING: 20 mins

8 frankfurter sausages
450g/1lb macaroni
60g/2oz butter or margarine
90g/3oz plain flour
560ml/1 pint milk
180g/6oz Cheddar cheese, grated
1 tsp dry mustard powder
Salt and pepper

1. Poach the frankfurters for 5-6 minutes in slightly salted boiling water.

2. Remove the skins from the frankfurters and, when cold, slice the meat diagonally.

3. Cook the macaroni in plenty of boiling salted water for about 10-15 minutes.

Step 2 Remove the skins from the frankfurters and cut them diagonally into slices about 2.5cm/1 inch long.

Step 6 Add the milk gradually, beating the mixture well between additions, until all the milk is incorporated.

4. Rinse in cold water and drain well.

5. Melt the butter in a saucepan. Stir in the flour and cook for 1 minute.

6. Remove the pan from the heat and add the milk gradually, beating thoroughly and returning the pan to the heat to cook between additions. When all the milk has been added, simmer for 2 minutes, stirring occasionally.

7. Stir in the frankfurters, grated cheese and mustard. Season to taste.

8. Add the drained macaroni to the sauce and stir well until heated through.

9. Pour the mixture into an ovenproof dish and sprinkle the top with a little extra grated cheese.

10. Cook under a preheated moderate grill, until the top is golden brown.

Lasagne Rolls

SERVES 4

An interesting way of using sheets of lasagne.

PREPARATION: 10 mins
COOKING: 15 mins

8 lasagne sheets
60g/2oz button mushrooms, sliced
225g/8oz boned chicken breast
30g/1oz butter, or margarine
30g/1oz plain flour
140ml/¼ pint milk
          Gruyère or Cheddar cheese, grated
Salt and pepper

1. Fill a large saucepan two thirds full with salted water. Add a little oil and bring to the boil.

2. Add 1 sheet of lasagne, wait about 2 minutes, then add another sheet. Cook only a few at a time and after about 6-7 minutes, remove and rinse under cold water. Allow to drain.

3. Repeat this process until all the lasagne is cooked.

4. Wash and slice the mushrooms, and slice the chicken breast into thin strips.

5. Melt half the butter in a small frying pan and fry the mushrooms and the chicken.

6. In a small saucepan, melt the rest of the butter. Stir in the flour and cook for 1 minute.

Step 11 Spread the chicken mixture evenly over each sheet of lasagne and roll up like a swiss roll.

7. Remove the pan from the heat and add the milk gradually, stirring well and returning the pan to the heat between additions, to thicken the sauce.

8. Beat the sauce well and cook for 3 minutes.

9. Pour the sauce into the frying pan with the chicken and the mushrooms. Add half the cheese and mix well. Season to taste.

10. Lay the sheets of lasagne on a board and divide the chicken mixture equally between them.

11. Spread the chicken mixture evenly over each lasagne sheet and roll up lengthways, like a swiss roll.

12. Put the rolls into an ovenproof dish. Sprinkle with the remaining cheese and grill under a pre-heated moderate grill, until the cheese is bubbly and golden brown.

Lasagne Napoletana

SERVES 6

This is lasagne as it is cooked and eaten in Naples.

PREPARATION: 25 mins
COOKING: 1-1¼hrs

9 sheets spinach lasagne

Tomato Sauce
3 tbsps olive oil
2 cloves garlic, crushed
900g/2lbs tinned tomatoes, drained
2 tbsps chopped fresh basil, six whole leaves
    reserved
Salt and pepper
Pinch sugar

Cheese Filling
450g/1lb ricotta cheese
60g/2oz unsalted butter
225g/8oz Mozzarella cheese, grated
Salt and pepper
Pinch nutmeg

1. Cook the pasta for 8 minutes in boiling salted water with a little oil. Drain and rinse under hot water and place in a single layer on a damp cloth. Cover with another damp cloth and set aside.

2. To prepare the sauce, cook the garlic in remaining oil for about 1 minute in a large saucepan. When pale brown, add the tomatoes, basil, salt, pepper and sugar.

Step 5
Carefully spread the softened cheese mixture on top of the tomato sauce.

3. Lower the heat under the saucepan and simmer the sauce for 35 minutes. Add more seasoning or sugar to taste.

4. Beat the ricotta cheese and butter together until creamy and stir into the remaining ingredients.

5. Place 3 sheets of lasagne on the base of a greased baking dish. Cover with one third of the sauce and carefully spread on a layer of cheese. Place another 3 layers of pasta over the cheese and cover with another third of the sauce. Add the remaining cheese filling and cover with the remaining pasta. Spoon the remaining sauce on top.

6. Cover with foil and bake for 20 minutes at 190°/375°F/Gas Mark 5. Uncover and cook for 10 minutes longer. Garnish with the reserved leaves and leave to stand 10-15 minutes before serving.

Fish Ravioli

SERVES 4

This ravioli dish is served with a subtly flavoured cream and lemon sauce.

PREPARATION: 30 mins
COOKING: 30 mins

Dough
275g/9oz strong plain flour
3 eggs

225g/8oz sole fillets
2 tbsps breadcrumbs
2 eggs, beaten
1 spring onion, finely chopped
1 slice of onion
1 slice of lemon
6 peppercorns
1 bay leaf
1 tbsp lemon juice
300ml/½ pint water

Lemon sauce
30g/1oz butter or margarine
30g/1oz flour
2 tbsps double cream
2 tbsps lemon juice

1. Pre-heat oven to 180°C/350°F/Gas Mark 4. Place fish in oven-proof dish with onion, lemon, peppercorns, bay leaf, lemon juice and water. Cover and cook for 20 minutes.

2. Remove fish from liquid, and allow to drain. Strain liquid, and set aside.

3. When fish is cool, beat to a pulp. Add 2 eggs,

Step 6 Shape the filling into small balls, and set them about 4cm/1½" apart on one half of the dough.

breadcrumbs and spring onion, and season.

4. Sift flour into a bowl and add the eggs. Work together with a spoon, then knead by hand, until smooth. Leave for 15 minutes.

5. Lightly flour a board, and roll out dough thinly into a rectangle. Cut dough in half.

6. Shape the filling into small balls, and set them about 4cm/1½" apart on one half of the dough. Place the other half on top, and cut with a ravioli cutter. Seal the edges.

7. Cook in batches in boiling salted water for about 8 minutes, then drain.

8. To make sauce, melt butter in a pan, then stir in flour. Draw off heat, and gradually stir in liquid from cooked fish. Return to heat and bring to boil. Simmer, add cream and mix well. Season.

9. Remove from heat, and gradually stir in lemon juice. Do not reboil. Pour sauce over ravioli and serve.

Cannelloni

SERVES 4

This tasty meat dish justifiably remains a favourite.

PREPARATION: 10 mins
COOKING: 1 hr

12 cannelloni shells
2 tbsps Parmesan cheese, grated

450g/1lb minced beef
1 tbsp olive oil
1 onion, peeled and chopped
2 cloves garlic, crushed
225g/8oz packet frozen spinach, thawed
½ tsp oregano
1 tsp tomato purée
4 tbsps cream
1 egg, lightly beaten

Tomato sauce
1 tbsp olive oil
1 onion, peeled and chopped
1 clove garlic, crushed
400g/14oz tin plum tomatoes
2 tbsps tomato purée

Béchamel sauce
300ml/½ pint milk
30g/1oz butter or margarine
30g/1oz flour

1. Heat the oil in a pan, and fry garlic and onion gently until soft and transparent.

2. Add meat and cook until well browned. Add

Step 4
Carefully fill the cannelloni with the meat mixture.

tomato purée, and oregano, and cook gently for 15 minutes.

3. Add spinach, egg and cream, and salt and pepper to taste.

4. Cook pasta in boiling salted water for 15-20 minutes. Rinse and drain. Fill with meat mixture.

5. To make the tomato sauce, heat the oil in a pan, add onion and garlic, and cook gently until transparent. Add tomatoes, tomato purée and season to taste. Bring to boil, and then simmer for 5 minutes. Set aside.

6. To make the Béchamel sauce, melt butter in pan. Remove from heat and stir in flour. Gradually add milk, and bring to boil, stirring continuously, until sauce thickens. Add seasoning.

7. Spread tomato sauce in an oven-proof dish. Lay pasta on top, and cover with Béchamel sauce. Sprinkle with Parmesan cheese, and bake at 180°C/350°F/Gas Mark 4 for 30 minutes.

Spinach Lasagne

SERVES 4

Spinach flavoured with nutmeg makes a delicious filling for lasagne.

PREPARATION: 10 mins
COOKING: 30 mins

---

8 sheets green lasagne

Spinach sauce
90g/3oz butter or margarine
325g/11oz packet of frozen spinach, thawed
   and chopped finely
Pinch of ground nutmeg
90g/3oz flour
150ml/¼ pint milk
Salt and pepper

Mornay sauce
30g/1oz butter or margarine
30g/1oz flour
300ml/½ pint milk
90g/3oz Parmesan cheese, grated
1 tsp French mustard
Salt

---

1. To make spinach sauce, heat butter in pan, stir in flour and cook for 30 seconds.

2. Draw off heat and stir in milk gradually.

3. Return to heat, and bring to the boil, stirring continuously. Cook for 3 minutes.

4. Add spinach, nutmeg, and salt and pepper to taste. Set aside.

Step 9 Line the base with a layer of lasagne, followed by some of the spinach mixture and a layer of cheese sauce.

5. Cook spinach lasagne in lots of boiling salted water for 10 minutes. Rinse in cold water and drain carefully. Dry on a clean cloth.

6. To make Mornay sauce, heat butter in pan and stir in flour, cooking for 30 seconds.

7. Remove from heat, and stir in milk. Return to heat, stirring continuously, until boiling. Continue stirring, and simmer for 3 minutes.

8. Draw off heat, and add mustard and two-thirds of cheese, and salt to taste.

9. Grease an oven-proof baking dish. Line the base with a layer of lasagne, followed by some of the spinach mixture, and a layer of cheese sauce.

10. Repeat the process finishing with a layer of lasagne with a covering of cheese sauce.

11. Sprinkle with the remaining cheese. Bake in a hot oven 200°C/400°F/Gas Mark 7 until golden on top. Serve immediately.

Index

Spaghetti with Tomato, Salami and Green Olives

MARTIN LUTHER

EXPLORING HIS LIFE AND TIMES, 1483–1546

Helmar Junghans

FORTRESS PRESS
MINNEAPOLIS

MARTIN LUTHER—EXPLORING HIS LIFE AND TIMES, 1483–1546

FORTRESS PRESS EDITION, 1998

Write to: Permissions, Augsburg
Fortress, Box 1209, Minneapolis, MN 55440.
Author: H. Junghans. Owned by assignment by Hänssler Publishing.
Interactive computer animation by mib GmbH (in collaboration with MedienLabor für kommunikative
Strategien e.V. and the MedienInstitut am Museumspädagogischen Dienst): Arthur Engelbert, Winfried
Gerling, Uta Ionescu, Alexander Kirchhof, Peter Lay, Reinhard Ludwig, Martin Mißfeldt, Markus
Ramershoven, Gösta Röver. Conceptual Design: Arthur Engelbert, Winfried Gerling; Programming:
Winfried Gerling, Reinhard Ludwig; Design: Winfried Gerling, Uta Ionescu, Peter Lay; Animated Film:
Martin Mißfeldt; Coordination of Materials: Ansgar Gerling, Gösta Röver; Text: Helmar Junghans; Texts
for the Themes: mib; Text Editing: mib; Translation of Text: Katharina Gustavs; Texts for Themes: Henry
Pickford; Image Captions and Editor: Scott Hendrix; Image Captions: Thekla Junghans; Image Editing:
mib; Musical Composition: Helix Musikproduktion, Berlin (Armin Köhrer, Andreas Roth); Speakers:
Nawroz Abbany (Film), Shaun Lawton (Luther), Yves Lawton (Nursery Rhymes); Chorals: Vocal Ensemble
of the Zwölf-Apostelkirche Schönenberg; Director: Hermann Hulman, Berlin; Recording: Helix Musikproduktion, Berlin; Photographs: Wilfried Kirsch, Ulrich Kneise. For their active participation, we thank:
Verena Hupasch, Julia Hofer, Oliver Ionescu, Ania Rudolph, Franz Tröger, Christopher Dehn. We especially thank: Thekla Junghans, Jutta Strehle, Petra Wittig (Luther-Hall, Wittenberg). For coordination we
thank: Manuela Rost-Hein (IBM).

FORTRESS PRESS ENGLISH EDITION   ISBN 0-8006-3147-1
Editorial and production: Joseph Bonyata; Additional English translation: Gene Janssen; Cover and book
design: Craig Claeys and Mike Mihelich.

Manufactured in the U.S.A.   AF 1-3147
03   02   01   00   99   1   2   3   4   5   6   7   8   9   10

PREFACE

MARTIN LUTHER DOMINATED PUBLIC opinion like no one else at the start of the sixteenth century. With the help of movable-type letterpress printing, his theses traveled to the farthest corners of the German Empire and circulated throughout Europe. Certainly his battle cry against the Roman Church struck the nerve of his time. His pastoral tractates in turn helped the simple Christian to lead his or her life in keeping with the principles of the Bible. Yet without the printing press, the voice of the Bible professor and preacher would have been confined to the small provincial town of Wittenberg. Printing with movable letters, invented by Gutenberg, sparked the first media revolution in Germany. Martin Luther endowed it with specific contents. Today we find ourselves in the midst of a second media revolution. And once again Luther provides its contents. For the Luther-Hall in Wittenberg, the largest museum in the world devoted to the history of the Reformation, it is a unique pleasure and honor to present here material about Luther's life and work in a way that speaks to both the scholarly world and the interested lay public. First we would like to thank the author of the CD-ROM, Helmar Junghans, one of the foremost scholars of Luther in Germany. Likewise, the team members at mib GmbH (in collaboration with the MedienInstitut am MD, Berlin) deserve great recognition for accomplishing this project. Finally, we would like to thank IBM Deutschland for their bold participation in this project.

—*Martin Treu*
Wittenberg, October 1996

THE READER AS USER

IS IT POSSIBLE TO REPRESENT LUTHER, the reformer and translator of the Bible, adequately in a multimedia environment? From the outset our challenge was to unite Luther's evaluation of the biblical word with the new possibilities of interlinked, digitized hypertext. The printed word speaks to the reader. The digitized text brings the user of the computer interface into play. The solution could only lie in rediscovering the reader in the "clicking user." Just as one takes a book in hand and concentrates on the text, so one turns on the computer, inserts the CD-ROM, starts the program, and attentively uses the interactive medium of the computer. In this CD-ROM we have preserved well-known organizational principles like chapters, categories, themes, and narrative sequences, though we have further developed the logical consistency of textual and visual passages.

The traditional reader has learned to comprehend the stages of Luther's life and his influence. Above and beyond that, the user, who is both reader and interactive participant in this CD-ROM, has the opportunity to interact with the material through numerous hyperlinks. Thus she can decide whether she would like, for instance, to learn more about certain persons or localities (for example, to study in more detail the animation about purgatory or a map of Rome). All the interactive references are designed with a central thematic motif as well as an organizing concept, and the many available options invite interruptions in the process of reading, observing, clicking, and listening. Each reader decides how much he will read, when he will open a book, and whether he will read further in it. The user, by contrast, integrates the possibilities for appropriating text and visual levels. She links them in the sequence of connections she chooses, generates her individual rhythm, follows her interests enthusiastically, remaining on the surface of the information or dipping below to learn even more.

—Arthur Engelbert
mib GmbH

4

CHAPTERS

Eight chapters constitute the organizing structure of this CD-ROM. They invite the user to learn about the life of Luther and his development as a reformer. Active concepts in the text connect the chapters to the categories.

FILMS

Entertaining animated films accompany the chapters, showing the periods of Luther's life.

THEMES

Luther's historical life is supplemented with topics that give a view of his time.

ENTRANCE LEVEL CATEGORIES

Eight categories allow the reader to move from a given chapter and explore in more detail different areas of knowledge and historical sources (over 1,000 visual, textual, and sound documents).

ORGANIZATION OF THE MARTIN LUTHER CD-ROM

1. Subject Headings (texts related to Luther's life)

2. Films (animated film clips on the subject headings)

3. Themes (texts on themes from each period)

4. Categories (in lexicon format)

NO.	SUBJECT HEADINGS	FILMS	THEMES	CATEGORIES
1	Childhood and Education	chapter	toys	biography
2	Monk, Journey to Rome, Professor of Theology	chapter	travels	pictures
3	Indulgences, Papal Bull, and Imperial Ban	chapter	purgatory	texts
4	Spread of the Gospel	chapter	printing	glossary
5	Rise of a Protestant Church	chapter	angels	legacy
6	Luther's Everyday Life	chapter	reading	music
7	Battle between God and the Devil	chapter	alchemy	chronology
8	Luther's Last Journey	chapter	life	places

2. Start-up Screen

Icons for subject headings, films, themes, and categories are arranged in rotating clockwise order on the start-up screen.

Clicking on an icon causes the chosen subject to appear.

The revolving icons are represented by the following signs:

★ Biography

👁 Legacy

🎞 Picture

♪ Music

A Text

𝟞 Chronology

⋮ Glossary

⛲ Places

7

The three icons at left (from left to right) have the following functions:

- Exit

- Move

- Highlighting the picture, leaving only the title line visible. With this feature the categories are still visible while one views another chapter heading or film.

In this example, the highlighted picture of the category "Places" is moved to the upper edge, and the last chapter heading appears in the center of the screen.

The alphabet appears under the framed category. By choosing the beginning letter of a subject, one can go directly to that subject without paging through lengthy documents.

At the top right, the above-mentioned symbols appear. Simply clicking on the symbols facilitates rapid navigation.

When a term or concept is found on the right side of the toolbar, to access this subject one must press ENTER or RETURN. After the entry of "Augsburg," for example, the picture at left appears.

With the two arrows one can navigate forward and backward through the entries (in ascending or descending alphabetical order).

Navigating the picture with the mouse will produce further explanations of commentary, for example, "Engraving from the Year 1552."

If more information is available, an arrow icon appears for further exploration.

Choosing one of the eight subject headings on the start-up screen brings up a screen with the subject heading text (in this example, the beginning of the subject).

A miniature version of the entire text appears on the left side of the screen. On the right the various descriptions of that portion of the text are given. The subject heading in large print at the top center of the screen is framed on the left (mini-mized version) to orient you within the document.

There are two ways to navigate through the document: (1) Click on the framed portion of the minimized text; or (2) Position the mouse at the middle of the bottom or top edge of the main text. The pointer changes into an arrow, and, by clicking the mouse button, the text will advance forward or backward.

3. Subject Headings

With the subject heading icons one can return to the toolbar or go to the desired subject heading, film, or theme.

In the texts, selected topics are highlighted (for example, names, places, or concepts). These can be accessed for more detailed information. If you click "Wittenberg," an icon appears with the concept over the middle of the main text. In this way, a type of reading mark is defined and a direct connection is made by just clicking on the icon.

Above the subject heading "Luther's Daily Life" appear the three icons "Luther, Katherine," "Bugenhagen, Johannes," and "WB Augustinian Cloister."

This procedure allows the user to read the complete text and at the same time mark various details.

4. Films

The films are accessed either by clicking on the appropriate text (see illustration), or by clicking on the "F" icon in the lower right edge of the screen.

In this example, we find the symbol as well as the text for the subject. On the right of the screen is a list of subject headings and subject summaries. The selection that the film illustrates is highlighted.

There are two ways to select a film:

1. By directly clicking on the subject heading on the right side of the screen.

2. By pointing with the mouse on the picture. The pointer will move from left to right in numbers from 1 to 8. Choices can be made by clicking the mouse button.

Text and music are audible through the speakers.

The eight themes are constructed and organized to be used individually.

    A. Toys

    B. Travels in Luther's Time

    C. Purgatory

    D. Printing Press

    E. Angel

    F. Reader

    G. Alchemy

    H. Life and Death

A. Toys

At the lower right are icons for connecting to subject headings, films, and categories. In this example, one can click on the fruits between the leaves. With each fruit, a different toy will be shown. The above example shows a picture of a toy from Luther's time.

B. Travels in Luther's Time

This opening screen displays travel options and conditions. The illustrations in the picture (coach, people, or the horse team) move from left to right or vice versa. Links to further information may be obtained by clicking on an illustration.

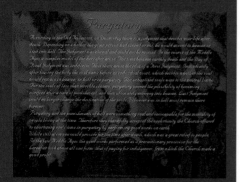

C. Purgatory

Click on the text and this picture appears.

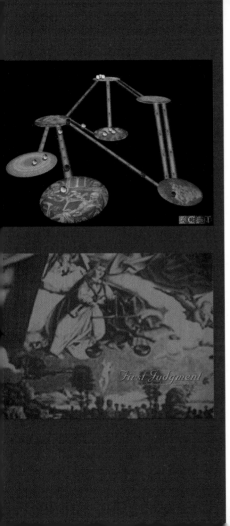

The marbles on each circular platform symbolize people and can be moved from one platform to another. The various platforms symbolize theological concepts according to the theories of Luther's time.

Clicking on a platform opens a picture of a concept, for example, "first judgment."

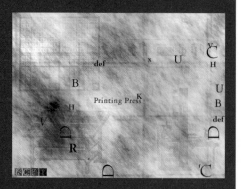

D. Printing Press

The theme of the printing press is presented in this screen. Navigating with the mouse (without clicking) over the illustrations reveals the texts for printing, Gutenberg, book press, and multiple printings.

Clicking on a particular letter will reveal further details about printing. The letters in the upper portion of the picture represent the initial letters for various categories of printing. By clicking on a letter, a further explanation appears in the lower portion of the screen.

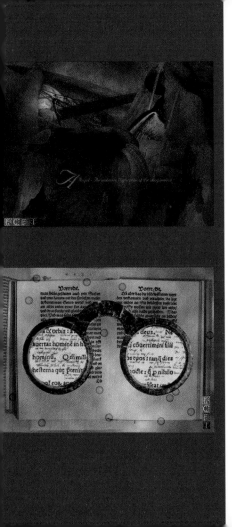

E. Angel

Clicking on the moving text of this screen brings up a general text about angels. Navigating with the mouse will access various segments. Repeated clicking will automatically reveal various illustrations of angels from that era.

F. Reader

Positioning the arrow on this picture will reveal various illustrations about reading. Further information is obtained by clicking on the lenses of the glasses. For example, clicking on the left lens brings up a text from a Reformation Era reader, and clicking on the right lens brings up a fictional bibliography.

G. Alchemy

This screen appears at first. After a short animation, it moves into the main menu.

Four possible links may be chosen from the three themes on the upper edge of the picture or by clicking on the circle in the middle of the picture.

The emerald table first appears as this.

And then appears as this.

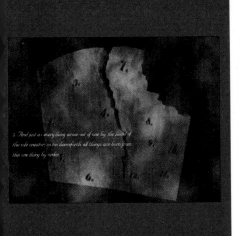

The Emerald Table is divided into twelve categories that express the twelve theses of magic. Navigating with the mouse to one of these categories/numbers opens the accompanying text, for example, a quote from Agrippa of Nettesheim.

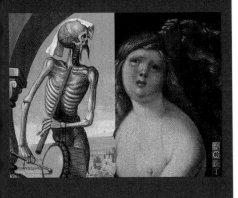

H. Life and Death

6. Categories

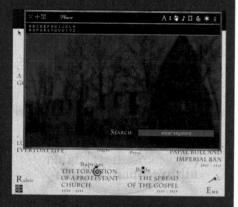

Choosing a category on the start-up screen opens the screen at left.

Textual documents, pictorial documents, and music are further subdivided.

The example of a textual document offers a list on the left: Letter, Printing, Incidental Remarks, and Table Talks. These are accessed by clicking the mouse.

Pictorial documents have the following choices:

- Picture
- Handwriting
- Title/Text
- Maps/Diagrams

The following choices are available in the Music category:

- Illustration
- Performance
- Notation

7. Index

Clicking on the "I" icon brings up the index. Clicking on the "E" icon in the lower-right-hand corner returns the user to the start-up screen.

Seven sections are available.

    A. Usage Pointers

    B. General Pointers

    C. Captions

    D. Abbreviations

    E. Subject Headings and Category Images

    F. Illustration Topics

    G. Printing Entire Chapters

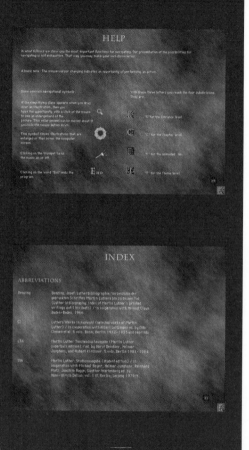

A. USAGE POINTERS
Navigate by clicking on the small arrow on the lower right of the screen.

B. GENERAL POINTERS
To page down, use the arrow on the left.

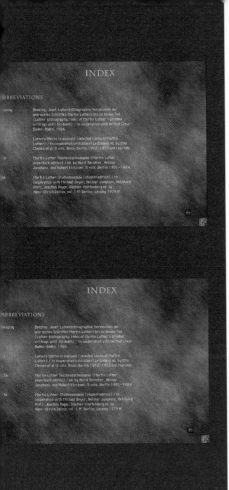

C. CAPTIONS

D. ABBREVIATIONS

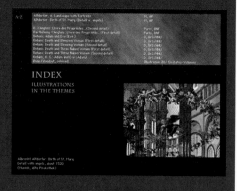

Albrecht Altdorfer: Birth of St. Mary
Detail with angels, about 1520
(Munich, Alte Pinakothek)

E. SUBJECT HEADINGS AND CATEGORY IMAGES

Choosing a letter of the alphabet at the left will produce an alphabetical listing of topics.

Clicking on a topic in the list will produce an illustration in the lower right of the screen.

Albert, Archbishop of Magdeburg and Mainz: Letter of Indulgence
The name of the buyer filled in the blank form
Parchment, 1515
(Lutherstadt Wittenberg, Lutherhalle)

F. ILLUSTRATION TOPICS

The same instructions as above apply here.

G. PRINTING ENTIRE CHAPTERS

Click on the chapter you want to print.

PRINT

MAP OF LUTHER'S WORLD

All important places connected with Luther or the Reformation are designated.

For example, how can I . . .

Find out about a city?

A. Start the CD

B. On the screen, click on the symbol for places (the tower)

C. In the upper left area of the alphabet click on the beginning letter of the city

D. Move the arrow to the desired city

E. Enter the name of the city in the search field

Find out more about a person?

A. Start the CD

B. On the screen click on the symbol for people/biography (the star)

C. In the upper left area of the alphabet click on the beginning letter of the person

D. Move the arrow to the desired person

E. Enter the name in the search field

Troubleshooting

This multimedia Martin Luther CD-ROM has been tested on various software and hardware configurations. If your system is configured properly, this application will perform without difficulties. However, some problems may arise with certain configurations. Some of the most common problems are described below with suggestions for possible solutions.

Program won't install

The program requires a minimum of 8 megabytes of RAM to run.

Close all applications before installation. Screen savers, anti-virus applications, clocks, and similar devices may disrupt installation.

Macintosh users should turn off all extensions except multimedia and CD-ROM drivers.

Program won't start or crashes immediately

Turn off your program before starting the Martin Luther CD-ROM. In Windows, press (at the same time) the **CTR** and ESC keys. This merges the list of the various drives. Close everything except Program Manager. Enter a comment in the task list and click the "On" icon. If Program Manager is the only item in the list, hit the ESC key.

Be sure that the CD is clean and the correct side is up.

If you are running Windows 3.11, be sure that your computer is compatible with Windows MSCDEX.EXE.

Troubleshooting

Pictures appear in unrealistic colors

Make sure that your computer supports the use of 256 colors. You will be able to find this information in your computer manual.

Videos do not run

Make sure you have the latest version of QuickTime installed on your computer, version 2.0 or higher on a Macintosh and version 2.01 or higher on an IBM PC or compatible computer.

If in doubt, reinstall the software

Certain high-speed, super-VGA drivers do not fulfill the specifications for Windows and can create problems during the replay of videos. Get the newest driver for your video card or use the general SVGA-driver produced by Microsoft.

Programs run slowly

Close all other programs.

Make sure that your computer has at least 16 MB RAM. For optimal performance in Windows, we suggest using at least 8 MB of virtual memory. Consult your Windows manual about configuring virtual memory.

Make sure you have a 2x (better yet, 4x or faster) CD-ROM drive. Single speed drives cannot process data fast enough to support video replay.

Troubleshooting

Program stalls

Program interruptions usually occur due to lack of memory. Stop working on the computer, turn it off and reboot. Before starting the Luther program, close all other active programs. Should interruptions still occur, you may need more memory.

Be sure your CD drive is working correctly. It may be necessary to clean the drive with a CD drive cleaner.

No sound is audible

Be sure that your system has a sound card that works properly.

Verify that the sound system is activated and that the volume is adjusted to an adequate level. Further information may be found in your computer or sound system manual.

If your speakers have separate volume controls, set these at an appropriate level.

When all else fails, call us

Before you call for technical support, determine the make, model, and operating system of your computer. Also know the amount of RAM and the type of video card, sound card, and CD-ROM drive. Document how the problem developed and which error messages occurred.

For technical support, please call:
Augsburg Fortress Technical Support (612) 330-3271
8 A.M. to 5 P.M. Central Time

ABOUT THE AUTHOR

HELMAR JUNGHANS, BORN IN 1931 IN Geyer near Dresden, is a member of the Lutheran Church, underwent a religious experience during his imprisonment under the Soviet military administration from 1947 to 1951 (1949 to 1950 in the former concentration camp at Sachsenhausen), and met the Luther scholar Franz Lau in Leipzig. He was ordained in 1964.

Since 1964 he has taught at the University of Leipzig, and since 1990 he has been university professor for church history in the theological faculty in Leipzig. He has received various academic honors, has been the editor of the Luther Yearbook since 1972, and has edited *Leben und Werk Martin Luthers von 1526–1546*, 2 vols., Berlin, 1983/1986. In 1995 he became a full member of the Sachsen Academy of Sciences in Leipzig.

His numerous publications include: *Ockham im Lichte der neueren Forschung* (Berlin, 1968), *Die Reformation in Augenzeugenberichten* (Munich, 1967), *Der junge Luther und die Humanisten* (Weimar, 1984), *Martin Luther und Wittenberg* (Munich, 1996).

SOFTWARE LICENSE AND LIMITED WARRANTY

SOFTWARE LICENSE

This software is intended for private use on a single-user computer or workstation. For multiple-user or network licensing, call Augsburg Fortress (612) 330-3271, 8 A.M. to 5 P.M. Central Time.

THIRTY DAY SATISFACTION GUARANTEE

For thirty (30) days after the invoice date or receipt date (if purchased at a retail location), you may return the complete product if you are dissatisfied with the software for any reason. To receive a full refund, you must return both the software and documentation with your invoice or receipt.

LIMITED WARRANTY FOR NINETY DAYS

Augsburg Fortress warrants that upon delivery the software will substantially conform to the documentation for it, provided that it is properly used on the computer hardware and with the operating system(s) for which it was designed. Augsburg Fortress also warrants that the software will be properly copied onto discs and that the discs on which the software is recorded will be free from defects in materials and workmanship under normal use and service for ninety (90) days from the invoice or receipt date.

AUGSBURG FORTRESS DISCLAIMS ALL OTHER WARRANTIES OF ANY KIND REGARDING THE SOFTWARE, DOCUMENTATION, AND DISCS, INCLUDING THE WARRANTIES OF MERCHANTABILITY AND FITNESS FOR A PARTICULAR PURPOSE.

LIMITATION OF LIABILITY

Neither Augsburg Fortress nor anyone involved in the creation, production, or delivery of this software or its contents shall be liable for any indirect, incidental, special, exemplary, or consequential damages, including but not limited to any loss of anticipated revenue, profit, or benefits, resulting from the use of the software or its documentation or arising out of any breach of warranty. Augsburg Fortress's cumulative liability to you or any other party for damages for any cause whatsoever will be limited to the price you paid for the Augsburg Fortress product that caused the damage.

White Fang

Retold from the Jack London
original by Kathleen Olmstead

Illustrated by Dan Andreasen

STERLING

New York / London
www.sterlingpublishing.com/kids

STERLING and the distinctive Sterling logo are registered trademarks of
Sterling Publishing Co., Inc.

Library of Congress Cataloging-in-Publication Data

Olmstead, Kathleen.
  White Fang / retold from the original story by Jack London; abridged by
Kathleen Olmstead; illustrated by Dan Andreasen; afterword by Arthur Pober
      p. cm.—(Classic starts)
Summary: An abridged version of the adventures in the northern wilderness
of a dog who is part wolf and how he comes to make his peace with man.
  ISBN 1-4027-2500-0
1. Dogs—Juvenile fiction. [1. Dogs—Fiction. 2. Wolves—Fiction.
3. Canada—Fiction.]   I. Andreasen, Dan, ill. II. London, Jack, 1876–1916.
White Fang. III. Title. IV. Series.

PZ10.3.O524Whi 2006
[Fic]—dc22

                                                           2005015761

Lot#:
2 4 6 8 10 9 7 5 3 1
01/11
Published by Sterling Publishing Co., Inc.
387 Park Avenue South, New York, NY 10016
Copyright © 2006 by Kathleen Olmstead
Illustrations copyright © 2006 by Dan Andreasen
Distributed in Canada by Sterling Publishing
$^{c}/_{o}$ Canadian Manda Group, 165 Dufferin Street
Toronto, Ontario, Canada M6K 3H6
Distributed in the United Kingdom by GMC Distribution Services
Castle Place, 166 High Street, Lewes, East Sussex, England BN7 1XU
Distributed in Australia by Capricorn Link (Australia) Pty. Ltd.
P.O. Box 704, Windsor, NSW 2756, Australia

Classic Starts is a trademark of Sterling Publishing Co., Inc.

Sterling ISBN 978-1-4027-7362-4

For information about custom editions, special sales, premium and
corporate purchases, please contact Sterling Special Sales
Department at 800-805-5489 or specialsales@sterlingpublishing.com.

CONTENTS

CHAPTER 1

A Seventh Dog

⌒

There was nothing but white as far as the eye could see. Snow and ice covered everything for miles and miles and miles. The trees, stripped bare by the harsh wind, made the land look even lonelier. It was hard to believe that anyone could survive in this place. It was the savage and bitter Wild of the North.

A team of dogs slowly pulled a sled along the frozen river. One man walked in front of the dogs and another man walked behind the sled. They all moved slowly. It was very hard work.

The men wore wide snowshoes, big heavy coats, wool hats, and mittens. Their breath froze in the air, coating their eyelashes and cheeks with ice crystals. There were no sounds other than their own footsteps in the snow. The two men felt very alone in this silent white land. They began to worry that they would never reach the safety of the next town.

They heard a faint cry in the still air. It slowly died away just as a second one rose. The front man turned his head to look at his friend. The cries were coming from somewhere behind them.

"I think they're after us, Bill," said Henry, the man up front.

"I know," Bill replied. He sounded worried. "Meat is scarce. I ain't seen a rabbit for days."

The two men continued to walk in silence, listening to the approaching howls behind them. They both knew there were plenty of reasons to be scared. A great famine was going through the Wild.

A wild wolf pack had been roaming the land for weeks looking for food. It was a new member of the pack who first noticed the two men and team of sled dogs. She was a red dog who had left her Indian village when food was scarce. She knew the sight and smell of man very well.

The days are very short during Northern winters. As darkness fell, the men led their dogs and sled near some trees. They built a fire and started dinner. Bill and Henry had made many trips along this river in the winter. They were used to the routine of traveling during the few daylight hours and camping at night. This time felt different, though. With the wolves following so close, they were more nervous about their journey.

The sled dogs gathered on the far side of the fire. They snarled and bickered with one another, but showed no signs of running off into the darkness. They knew fire meant warmth and safety in the Wild.

After Bill fed the dogs, he returned to eat his own supper. His friend handed him a plate of beans.

"Henry," Bill said. "How many dogs do we have?"

"Six," Henry said. "Why?"

"Well, I took out six fish to feed them and I didn't have enough for all the dogs."

"You must have counted the fish wrong," said Henry.

"No, no, I had six fish. There were seven dogs over there," Bill said. "I saw one run off after it got the fish."

"Then you're thinking it was—" Henry's sentence was cut short by another cry in the darkness. They both sat perfectly still as they listened. Their sled dogs started to panic as the tiny camp was surrounded by howls. Bill threw more wood on the fire.

"So, you think it was a wolf from that pack?" Henry pointed out into the darkness. "He'd have to be pretty tame to get in that close," Henry added. Bill shook his head. "Didn't look like a wolf to me. Seemed more like a dog."

"A dog?" Henry said. "What's a dog doing out here?"

Bill started to reply, but he stopped. He thought he saw something moving just past the light of the fire. He nudged Henry. They looked into the darkness and saw eyes—several pairs of eyes—staring back at them.

The red dog took the lead of the wild pack. She had spent many hours near campfires and knew the feeling of warmth and comfort a fire provided. The flames, however, frightened the wolves. In the Wild, fire meant danger; it was something to avoid. But they were starving, so they took the red dog's lead and tried to move in closer.

"Check for bullets, Bill," Henry said. "How many do we have left?"

"Three," Bill replied. "We've only got three bullets left." Without saying another word, both men knew they were in trouble.

They tried to stay awake to keep watch, but they were too tired. Also, they knew that the next day would be just as difficult. They would need a great deal of energy to travel over the ice. They bundled into their sleeping bags and fell asleep. The two men felt confident that the campfire would keep the wolves away.

CHAPTER 2

An Accident

Bill woke up with the first light of dawn. After a quick inspection of his dogs, he nudged Henry awake.

Henry could see immediately that his friend was upset. "What's wrong now?" he asked.

"All right," Bill said. "How many dogs did you say we had?"

"Six."

"Wrong," Bill said.

"Seven again?" Henry asked.

"No, five. One's gone."

"Did the wolves get him?" Henry felt very worried.

"I guess so," Bill shrugged.

Henry jumped up to look. Bill was right. One of their dogs was gone. Now they had only five dogs to make it across the snow and ice.

The two men quickly repacked their sled and set off with the dogs. Once again they barely spoke, saving their energy for the hard work. They made good time despite the bumpy ground. The sled almost turned over several times but Henry and Bill refused to stop. They did not want to spend another night in the Wild. But they were still far from the next village when disaster struck.

Rattling over ice and snow, the sled tipped and broke one of its runners. Henry and Bill couldn't repair it without the proper tools. Their only choice was to head out on foot. It was impossible to carry or drag all of their supplies, so they bundled up everything they couldn't carry and placed them high in a tree. Perhaps they would be able to come back for them later or someone else could use them. Men often left stores of supplies and food to pick up on their return journey. Henry wrote a note saying, "Take what you need. We left what we couldn't carry." He stuck it inside the top flap of their bundle. Taking hold of their remaining dogs, Henry and Bill continued down the frozen waterway.

One of the dogs, Spanker, kept trying to pull away, but Bill held on tightly. "Something's drawing him out," he said. Bill scanned the land around them. There was not much daylight left. He was not looking forward to another night huddled around the fire.

He stopped suddenly. "Henry," he whispered. "Look over there!"

Following at a distance behind them was the red dog. She stopped when they did, waiting to see what would happen next.

"She looks awful red for a wolf," Henry said. "And she's pretty big."

"Looks more dog than wolf, I'd say," Bill replied. And Bill was right. Although he did not want to get too close, he knew it was the same strange dog from the fire. She did not seem to be nervous around them. Bill wondered if she had ever lived with humans. She looked too tame for an animal from the Wild.

While they all waited, Spanker took the opportunity to pull quickly on his rope. He gained his freedom and ran toward the red dog. They approached each other slowly, moving in circles and sniffing. Spanker lowered himself as she came closer. Everything looked innocent enough, but the men knew there would be trouble.

In a flash, Spanker was surrounded by the wolf pack. He barked and snapped, but they kept drawing nearer. Bill raised his rifle and fired a single shot. The wolves scattered, but Spanker ran

with them. The two men called for him, but he was gone. They listened to his barks getting further away in the distance for a few minutes before heading off. There was nothing else to do.

"I thought Spanker had more sense than that," said Henry.

"Nah," Bill answered. "He was always a fool of a dog."

"Those wolves looked pretty skinny. And there were a lot of them, too."

"I know. It means they'll soon be back looking for food."

The two men marched through the snow for the rest of the day. The sun was already setting by three o'clock, so Henry and Bill decided to make camp. They realized that a roaring fire might be their only protection. The wolves were growing braver as they became even more desperate for food.

CHAPTER 3

The Attack

⌒

Henry was stirring the beans over the fire when he heard the sled dogs suddenly snap and growl. He looked over the flames and saw them scatter around the fire. By the time he reached them, one more was missing. Bill rushed to his side.

"Frog's gone," Henry said. "And he was the strongest of the bunch."

Bill looked out into the darkness, searching for movement or eyes too close to camp. The pack of wolves started to howl again, sending the sled dogs into further panic. The wolves were all around the small camp. Bill knew they were surrounded. They were in a great deal of danger. "Looks like we won't be sleeping very well tonight," said Bill.

Henry and Bill took turns keeping watch and sleeping. It was a restless night and both men were very nervous. Every sound startled them. They looked around quickly every time a sled dog whimpered or moved. First one sled dog ran off, then another. They had no way of knowing if they joined the wolf pack, were eaten, or took their chances in the Wild. With any luck, they found their way to the next village.

The red dog from the wolf pack was the first one to jump toward the fire. The other wolves, once again, followed her lead. They took turns running at the men, trying to knock them down.

Henry and Bill held their ground. They

grabbed sticks from the fire and swung them at the attacking animals. The wolves yelped as the flames hit them. But this only stopped them for a bit. As the night wore on, they came in closer and more often. Each leap toward the men was met with a swing of the club.

Bill shot the rifle at one of the wolves, but missed. He thought better about wasting another bullet—their last!—in the dark.

Henry moved the burning logs into a circle. He grabbed Bill's arm and pulled him into the ring of fire. It was very hot standing inside the circle, but it was certainly better than fending off the wolves with sticks. The starving animals continued in their attempts to reach the men, but the flames pushed them back every time.

In the morning, the wolves were still skulking close by. The last two sled dogs had run off and the men were now alone.

The red dog stood farther back. She watched the wolves circle the men or leap at the fire. She seemed to know that something would happen soon. Either the men would try to escape or one of the wolves would make it across the fire.

CHAPTER 4

Rescued

⟳

The fire was getting low and there was no more wood. "The trees," Henry said. He pointed toward the spruce trees standing twenty feet from their campsite.

Bill nodded. He pointed his rifle at a group of wolves and fired. He nicked one on its hind leg. It stumbled and yelped in pain while the others scattered. Henry and Bill raced toward the spruce trees. They ran faster than they ever had before. In mere seconds they were each high up in a tree, watching the wolves circle and howl below.

The wolves started to fight among themselves. The red dog snapped and growled at any who came near her. A large gray wolf—the leader of the pack—nipped at the heels of the other wolves. He encouraged them to find a way to get the men. And he was keeping them away from the red dog. His gesture was unnecessary, though. No one could get close to her.

It was hours later when the wolves heard something in the distance. The red dog was the first to stop and listen. She quickly understood and ran off in the opposite direction. The wolf pack followed. Henry and Bill waited, wondering what could have scared them off.

A half a dozen men approached on sleds. Henry and Bill could not believe their luck. They shouted and waved to the men.

"Up here!" Henry called. "You came just in time!"

The sled stopped beneath the trees. One of the men called, "What are you doing up there?"

"A r-red d-d-dog," Bill stuttered. "She lured our sled dogs away. A pack of wolves tried to get us."

They helped Henry and Bill down. The two men hugged their rescuers. There was not much time for questions and answers, though. Both men fell asleep almost immediately, worn out from their adventure. While the other men set up camp and started supper, Henry and Bill snored loudly on blankets.

By this time the wolf pack was already far away. It was on a new trail, hoping to pick up another scent in the frozen Wild. As the moon rose in the sky, the wolves ran swiftly through the woods. The story of Henry and Bill was now over, while the story of the red dog and the wolves was just beginning.

CHAPTER 5

Choosing a Mate

こうの

The wolf pack ran back up the riverside and into the woods, continuing its search for food. Tempers were short and the wolves snapped impatiently at one another.

The red dog was especially quick to bite or bark at any who came too close. Although she was not the leader, she held a special place in the pack. She had been the first to notice the two men and their sled dogs. She had also led the wolves to the camp and fire. And thanks to her watchful gaze, she had quickly warned the wolves when other men approached.

The leader of the pack was a large gray wolf. He was the winner of many fights and had the scars to prove it. He was even missing his right eye. One Eye snapped at any younger members who tried to pass him or run too close. The red dog, however, fell in beside him as though it were her rightful place. He did not snap or snarl at her. In fact, he seemed quite pleased. He touched the side of her neck with his nose while they trotted across the snow.

Other male wolves sought the red dog's attention, but One Eye pushed them back. Any wolf who challenged the leader was risking a fight. Many tried to take the lead from One Eye or to win the affection of the red dog, but none succeeded. It was all a part of the Wild. One Eye had worked and fought hard to become the leader of the pack. He would not give up his position easily.

One day the wolves ran into a clearing and One Eye stopped short. The rest of the pack followed his lead, waiting to see what he would do next. A moose was standing a few hundred feet away. The pack quickly fell into formation and ran in for the kill. All of the wolves—and the red dog—surrounded the giant animal and chased it down. The moose weighed well over eight hundred pounds. It was more than enough to feed everyone. At long last the famine was over. The wolves were now back in the land of game.

The pack started to break up. Two by two, male and female, the wolves began to leave. It was time to decide who would be the red dog's mate. One Eye made it very clear that no one else should even try. When a younger wolf nuzzled against the red dog's neck, One Eye quickly attacked him. The fight did not last long. The young wolf ran off and One Eye returned to the red dog. He had won her loyalty fair and square.

The Wild was a harsh place. The wolves' Rules were not the rules of humans. The wolves did not question the Rules or even understand them. They were simply rules that they must follow.

Now that it was just the two of them, the red dog once again found food. She led One Eye to an Indian village where they could raid food stores and rabbit traps. She taught One Eye how to pull the ropes from the trees and grab the rabbits from the traps. She knew how to steal meat cooking on fires and where fish was kept near the tents. The sights and smells of the camp were strange to One Eye, but every detail was familiar to the dog. She stood on the edge of camp, listening and waiting for something or someone. She whimpered softly as she watched the men and women of the camp sitting by the fire and talking. Only with much prodding from One Eye did she return to the woods.

After a time, the red dog started to slow down. She was getting very heavy and it was difficult to keep pace with her mate. She needed someplace safe and dry to settle down and have her puppies. She found a cave a few miles up a small stream. It was partway up a hill and safe from other animals. She went in carefully, searching for signs of life. She found none.

One Eye treated her with care. Once she was settled in, he brought her food and guarded the door while they waited.

Five puppies were born—four girls and one boy. The red dog licked them clean while One Eye looked on. The puppies let out tiny cries while taking their first breaths.

The boy was different from his sisters. They all had their mother's reddish fur, but he was all gray. He looked just like his father.

For the first while, the puppies lived in a world of darkness, as their eyes were still shut. They knew only the smells and sounds of the cave and their mother's gentle touch. The boy cub quickly got used to his surroundings, finding his way to and from his mother, listening for his father to come home. He and his sisters rolled and played with each other, waiting to be fed, discovering new sounds all around them.

Slowly, their eyes started to open. They could see their mother at last. They explored the cave, sniffing in all the corners and climbing on all the rocks. They didn't go near the entrance, though. Whenever they walked too far in that direction, the red dog quickly pulled them back. To their young eyes and innocent minds, they thought it was another wall. They had no idea another world existed beyond the wall of light. All they knew was the cave.

As the seasons changed, another famine hit

the land. Every day One Eye searched long and hard for meat to bring to his family. There was little to be found, though, and certainly not enough to feed so many mouths. The puppies became weaker and could no longer play or roam about the cave.

The red wolf went out hunting, too, but could find nothing. It was very difficult for her to watch her puppies grow weak. She knew in her heart that the Wild was a harsh place and that she must learn to accept it. She whimpered sadly when she came home from a hunt to find only one puppy left. It was the gray cub. She snuggled in close to keep him warm, doing everything she could to save the life of her only pup.

At long last, One Eye was successful. He killed a bird and brought it back to the cave. Things became easier again. Both parents went out for food and came back with enough to help the gray cub. Soon he was a healthy pup again, bounding

around the cave. He had survived his first famine, although it wouldn't be his last.

All was well until one day One Eye did not come home. The red dog knew something was wrong. She left the cave to look for him and found the lifeless body of her mate a few miles away. He had lost a battle with a lynx.

The red dog spent a few moments sniffing One Eye and saying goodbye. Suddenly she realized that her cub was all alone in the dangerous Wild. What if the lynx found its way to the cave? Anything could have happened while she was away. The red dog ran back to the cave as fast as she could.

CHAPTER 6

Exploration

∽

The gray cub spent a lot of time alone while his mother went hunting. He still had not gone beyond the mouth of the cave. As a matter of fact, he did not even know it was an opening. In his mind it was just another cave wall, except that his mother could walk through it. The wolf cub thought his mother could do anything. His father had left that way and had never come back. If the cub ever wandered too close to the entrance, his mother would nudge him back, sometimes with a soft growl as a warning. The cub always did as his mother wished. He knew that she was worried something might happen to him if he went too close to the entryway. Although he had never known danger, he knew fear. It was a part of his heritage. It was a part of the Wild. Fear would teach the wolf cub many valuable lessons.

A wolf does not think like a human. The cub did not look at the cave opening and wonder what was out there. It did not even occur to him. He knew only the world around him. But every day after his mother left in search of food, he moved closer to the exit. He smelled and heard new things with each step. Just as fear was a part of his heritage, so was the need to wander and hunt. When the day finally came that the white wall dissolved into colors—trees, the sky, a stream running through the woods—he stepped bravely outside. The cub blinked his eyes against the bright sunlight. What was this place?

Suddenly, a great fear came upon him. He crouched down on the lip of the cave and gazed out into the unknown, unfriendly world. The hair along his back stood up on end. His lips wrinkled weakly in an attempt at a fierce snarl. But then nothing happened.

The cub looked over the green trees into the blue sky. He watched a bird float above the trees then dive into the woods. It disappeared as it passed into the trees and the cub wondered what happened to it. He watched clouds move slowly across the sky. He felt a soft breeze on his muzzle. While he explored this new world, becoming more and more curious, he forgot to snarl. He also forgot to be afraid.

So he stepped boldly from the cave door— and fell forward, hitting his nose on the earth as he tumbled down the hill. He did not understand what it meant to fall. He rolled down the slope, over and over. He was in a panic. The unknown had caught him at last.

He stopped rolling when he reached the bottom of the slope. The gray cub sat up, confused and frightened. He licked his fur clean of mud and dirt. He was not hurt, only scared. He had broken through the wall of the world outside and survived.

He looked at the grass beneath him, stuck his nose in the bushes, and lifted his head high to feel the breeze. A squirrel running around a tree almost ran into him. It gave him a great fright. This was the first animal he had ever seen aside from his family. The cub cowered down and snarled, but the squirrel was just as scared. It ran up a tree. From that point of safety it chattered back fiercely.

This boosted the cub's confidence. Even though he was startled by more things as he walked along—a woodpecker, a branch that struck him in the face, the sound of a strange animal in the distance—he didn't shy away. He felt so brave, in fact, that when a moosebird hopped up to him, he reached out with a playful paw. The bird responded with a sharp peck on the end of the cub's nose. He yelped in pain and the bird quickly flew off.

The cub was learning. His mind was starting to sort this new world into different, useful groups. There were live things—like the bird and the squirrel—that he should be careful around. Then there were things not alive—like the cave and rocks that remain in one place. The live things moved about and there was no telling what they might do. He must always be prepared.

He walked very clumsily. He ran into bushes and shrubs, tripped over rocks, and stumbled into trees. But with every step he was learning more, and with every step he was more curious. This also led to more surprises.

He followed a strange sound through the leaves and came upon a stream. He stuck his paw in the water. It was wet and cool and entirely new. He put another paw in, then all four. The gray cub felt the current move around him. It was just like taking his first steps from the cave. Suddenly the ground below him disappeared and, crying with fear, he went down once again into the unknown.

He lifted his head out of the water and—as if he had been doing it all his life—he began to swim. He tried to turn around and head back to shore, but the current got hold of him and took him downstream. He was both terrified and excited by this new adventure. Everything was new and everything was scary.

When the current brought him close to some rocks, he pulled himself up. The gray cub crawled to shore and shook himself to dry off. He had no idea where he was or how to get home. He thought of his mother. He wanted her more than anything else in the world. He wondered how he would ever find her again. He started off, hoping he was walking in the right direction.

Just then a flash of yellow zipped past him. It was a weasel swiftly leaping out of his way. He was not afraid, only shocked and curious. He noticed an even smaller live thing—a baby weasel—very nearby. He leaned in to sniff this new creature and gently nudged it with his paw. Maybe this baby weasel would play with him. Suddenly the mother weasel came back. She was at the cub's side and quickly knocked him down.

The gray cub yelped. The mother weasel made a terrible and frightening noise as she stood over him. She swiped at him and tried to bite him in the neck. She did not understand that the gray cub meant no harm. She only thought about protecting her baby.

The gray cub would have died right then, and there would have been no story to write about him, had not the red dog come bounding through the bushes. The weasel turned to face this new threat, but the red dog was too quick. She grabbed the weasel with her teeth and shook violently. The dog then tossed the weasel back into the trees, far away from her pup.

Her joy at finding the gray cub seemed greater even than his joy at being found. She nuzzled him and caressed him and licked the wounds made in the weasel's attack. The gray cub whimpered and softly growled—a sweet, low rumbling in his throat—as he snuggled into his mother. He felt safe and happy at last.

CHAPTER 7

The Rule of the Wild

The cub grew in size and learned very quickly. He learned when to be bold and when to shy away. His mother took him on her hunts and the cub followed her example. His mother taught him that the Rule of the Wild was much more than "eat or be eaten." A wolf kills only when it is hungry or in danger. Even enemies must have respect for one another.

His mother let him roam and hunt on his own. She knew he had to discover some things for himself, although he never strayed too far from the cave. After his first great adventure, the cub was very careful not to get lost again. It was on one of his solo trips that the little wolf cub first encountered humans.

He was running down to the stream to get a drink of water. Still just an excited puppy, he burst through the bushes where, sitting silently by the water were five strange creatures. He tumbled along the riverbank rocks as he tried to stop. None of the men jumped up at the sight of him. Nor did they show their teeth or snarl. They simply sat there in silence. They were nothing like any of the other animals in the Wild. They did not follow any rules that the wolf cub understood.

The cub did not move either. His instincts told him to run, but something had caught hold of him. He was in awe. Something inside him said that he should respect these men. He sank down and cowered as one approached. When the man leaned in, the cub snarled and bared his fangs.

"Look!" the man laughed. "The white fangs!" He put his hand out to touch the cub's head. The young wolf moved quickly, biting the man's hand and drawing blood.

The man yelped and jumped back. "He bit me!"

His friends laughed at him. "What did you expect?" one of them asked.

The man, embarrassed and angry, struck the cub with a stick. The wolf cried in pain. He had never been hit before. He was confused about what was happening to him. The man would have continued beating the cub were it not for the red dog. At that very moment, she jumped from the bushes, teeth bared, ready to defend her son.

One of the other men spoke up at the sight of her. He looked toward the cub's mother and called, "Kiche!" The red dog stopped. She turned to the man who spoke. Her ears perked up at the sound of his voice. "Kiche," he said again. "Come here!"

And then the cub saw his mother, the fearless one, crouch down until her belly touched the ground. She whimpered and wagged her tail. The man who had spoken came over. He put his hand on her head and she crouched lower. She neither snapped nor threatened to snap. The other men came up and felt her. She did nothing to stop them.

"She ran away a year ago," said the man. His name was Gray Beaver. His brother had owned the red dog—whose name was Kiche—before she left for the Wild. "She ran away during a famine, when there was very little food for anyone, animal or man. Her father was a wolf, you know. It's not so strange that she would take to the Wild."

Gray Beaver tied a rope around Kiche's neck. She did not struggle or growl. In fact, she whimpered in delight and wagged her tail. Gray Beaver looked at the wolf cub still crouched on the ground. "Since my brother died in the winter, she and her pup are now mine," he said. None of the other men objected.

He reached down to grab the pup's scruff but was met with a growl and bared fangs. Gray Beaver laughed. "Brave boy. You like showing your teeth, huh? Well, then, your name will be White Fang." He led Kiche away from the stream and tied her to a tree. White Fang, as the cub was now called, followed and lay down beside his mother. If she gave in to these men then he must, too.

Gray Beaver put a hand on White Fang's back and rolled him over. Kiche looked on while the man rubbed the cub's belly. The cub felt strange and silly, lying on his back with his legs sprawled in the air. It was a position of such helplessness that White Fang's whole nature fought against it. He could do nothing to defend himself. He couldn't escape. But soon the fear settled down

and he noticed something new. He enjoyed having his belly rubbed. This was an entirely new experience for him and he liked it.

This pleasant moment was disturbed by the sound of strange noises approaching. The rest of the Indian tribe was arriving to set up camp. Many people appeared from the woods carrying supplies and food. Dogs and children ran through the camp as tents were put up and fire pits were dug. Suddenly White Fang was surrounded by activity and noise. There were too many things happening all at once. The wolf cub tried to take everything in, but it was impossible. He was about to start the next phase of his young life. One ruled more by man than by the Wild.

CHAPTER 8

A New Way of Life

White Fang had a new challenge before him—
other dogs. Wolves and dogs were cousins, but
they were very different. Dogs had lived with
humans for so long that most of their Wild heritage was lost. Wolves, on the other hand, did not
understand the feeling of belonging to anyone.
They were used to moving at their own pace and
going wherever they liked. White Fang had a lot
to learn about the Rules of Dogs.

As soon as the dogs saw White Fang and Kiche,
they attacked. The cub met them with bared teeth

and snarls, but he was no match. They piled on White Fang. There was a mass of growling, angry dogs with teeth gnashing against fur. Kiche strained against her leash, trying to reach the fight. White Fang bit at the oncoming legs and bellies. They knew that the wolf cub was different— that he was not all dog. They knew he was from the Wild and an outsider. They wanted him to know who was boss in the camp. The men stepped in, yelling and pulling the dogs apart.

In a few seconds, White Fang was back on his feet. He shook himself off and went to stand by his mother. He was not badly hurt. He only had a few scrapes, but he was shaken up. Why had these dogs tried to hurt him? Why did his mother not try to help him? He watched as the men pushed the dogs back with clubs. Although he did not know the word "justice," he was beginning to understand its meaning. His respect for man— and his mistrust of dogs—was growing.

Gray Beaver took Kiche and White Fang to his tent. White Fang looked inside his new master's home. This tent looked very much like the cave. It was dark and dry and quite warm. It smelled very different, though. White Fang was not used to the smell of cooked meat or dried animal hides or humans. These strange new animals did not smell like anything in the Wild. The cub stepped back, afraid and confused. He belonged outside and would stay there.

Gray Beaver's wife Kloo-kooch and son Mit'sah were settling in. They secured the tent and set up their beds and family goods inside. They worked without talking. They had pulled down and put up the tent so many times that it was second nature to them. They moved with the seasons, following game and avoiding the worst of the weather. Kloo-kooch gave a fish to each of the dogs while Gray Beaver built a fire.

White Fang watched his new master with

great interest. What was he doing? A strange light came from his hands. White Fang moved in closer. This light was also warm. It twisted and flickered around the sticks and moss. White Fang knew nothing about fire. It drew him as the light in the mouth of the cave had drawn him when he had been a young puppy. He crawled the several steps toward the flame. He heard Gray Beaver chuckle above him. White Fang stuck out his tongue to taste this strange light. The flames flickered against his nose and tongue.

He stumbled backward. He burst into yelps and cries as he rolled on the ground. Kiche barked and pulled on her leash, angry that she could not come to his aid. Gray Beaver, however, laughed loudly and slapped his thighs. He told everyone in the camp the story of White Fang trying to lick the flames. Soon everyone was laughing at the gray cub. The more he yelped and cried, the more they laughed.

White Fang was embarrassed. He did not like
people laughing at him. How could his yelps be
so funny? White Fang learned to hate the sound
of laughter. It was one more reason not to trust
others.

Kiche had lived with man before, so she tried
to teach her puppy about these new creatures.
Just as she had led him through life in the Wild,
she would now lead him through life with man.
He learned to read body language and listen to
tone of voice. He could also sense a great deal
through smell. A dog could sense if someone was
scared or angry or threatening. It was a special gift
that only dogs shared—and some wolves.

Watching his mother also taught him to follow his master's command. The red dog, who was
so brave and strong in the Wild, was now content
in the Indian camp. She wagged her tail whenever
Gray Beaver came near. She barked happily when

Kloo-kooch brought her dinner. White Fang was confused by the change in his mother, but he did not question it.

He went to sleep that night under a tree. He curled up near Kiche, who was still tied up. The sounds of the Indian camp slowly faded away. White Fang was full from dinner and warm from the fire. It had been a very tiring day. First he met the men, then had a fight with a group of dogs, then burned his tongue on the flames. He was exhausted.

He fell asleep to the sounds of his mother breathing and campfires crackling nearby. White Fang did not know that his life had changed forever. He would never live in the cave and hunt with his mother again. He went to sleep wondering, "What will the new day bring?"

CHAPTER 9

Lip-lip

$\sim$

As White Fang was very smart, it did not take him long to learn the ways of the camp—and whom to avoid. He learned that women would give him extra food when no one else was watching. He lingered near tents as meals were prepared, waiting for an extra fish or piece of meat to be thrown his way. Children, on the other hand, were often mean and threw things at him. Somehow he always got into trouble whenever he went too close to them. He was the center of too many jokes. And he learned to stay away from other dogs, Lip-lip in particular.

Lip-lip was older than White Fang and not happy about the newcomer. Lip-lip was a bully and liked bossing around the puppies. He took every chance to jump on or bother White Fang. The wolf cub was under constant attack. If he wandered around camp, sniffing in corners and under tent flaps, Lip-lip was waiting for him. He bit at the cub or knocked him over. White Fang rarely had a moment's peace. There was no time for puppy games when faced with Lip-lip and his attacks. White Fang was forced to grow up too quickly.

Since his mother was still tied up, Gray Beaver was his only defender. The other men in the camp blamed White Fang for every fight, every stolen piece of fish, and every overturned plate. He often hid behind Gray Beaver's legs while men pointed

fingers or waved clubs. His master never let anyone touch White Fang, even when it was the
cub's fault. And it sometimes was his fault. It is
hard to be fair and honest when no one treats
you that way.

White Fang missed the Wild. There were days
when he sat at the edge of camp and looked out
into the trees. But he always returned, restless and
uncomfortable, to whimper softly at Kiche's side.

Finally the day came when Gray Beaver
untied Kiche. White Fang was very happy about
his mother's freedom. He accompanied her joy-
fully around the camp. As long as he stayed close
by her side, Lip-lip kept his distance. For the first
time since coming to the camp, White Fang felt
happy and confident. At long last, things would
change. His mother was free and they could
return to their life in the Wild.

He led his mother to the edge of the woods.

The stream, the cave, and the quiet woods were calling to him. He ran on a few steps, stopped, and looked back. Kiche had not moved. He ran under some bushes playfully, trying to pull her out. There was something calling to him out there in the open. His mother heard it, too. But she also heard the call of fire and man. Kiche turned and slowly trotted back toward camp.

What was White Fang to do? After all, he was still a puppy. Although the call of the Wild was strong, the need to be with his mother was stronger. He followed her back to Gray Beaver's tent and the life of the camp, both good and bad.

Unfortunately, White Fang's life was about to change yet again. During the winter famine, Gray Beaver bought some meat from Three Eagles, another man from the tribe. In order to pay him back, Gray Beaver gave his friend some cloth, a bearskin—and Kiche. Three Eagles and his family were leaving camp to go trading in the South. He packed his new cloth and bearskin and led Kiche away by a rope.

White Fang watched while this strange man took his mother into a canoe. He was terrified. He barked and howled and ran up and down the shore. He tried to follow, but Three Eagles kicked him back. The man pushed the canoe into the water and set off.

Gray Beaver tried to hold onto the cub, but White Fang wiggled free. He ran into the river and started to swim after his mother.

Gray Beaver quickly grabbed another canoe

and chased White Fang. He was soon beside the frantic cub. The man reached in, grabbed him by the scruff of his neck and pulled him into the canoe. White Fang yelped and howled, calling for his mother. He tried to jump back into the water, but Gray Beaver stopped him. And then White Fang experienced something entirely new. Gray Beaver beat him. He delivered one slap after another until the cub stopped crying.

White Fang tried to growl and bare his teeth, but Gray Beaver was not afraid. There was nothing the wolf cub could do. He stopped growling and sat at Gray Beaver's feet as they returned to shore.

White Fang went home with his master. He understood that Gray Beaver was powerful and must be obeyed. But the wolf cub was no longer happy. He was more suspicious of people and other dogs. He liked to be on his own. The beatings and the loss of his mother changed him. They taught him that he must be mean.

CHAPTER 10

A Work Dog

⌒

It was time for White Fang to go to work. Life in the North was harsh and everyone—including dogs—had to help out. Gray Beaver and Mit'sah started training the new puppies—including White Fang—as sled dogs.

There were seven puppies on the team. The others had been born earlier in the year and were nine and ten months old, while White Fang was only eight months old. He worked on Mit'sah's team with Lip-lip as his leader.

They started off on small trips. It took them a

while to get used to pulling the sled. At first they tumbled over one another. The reins tangled around their legs and the straps slipped off their chests. Mit'sah had to stop the team several times to pull one of them out of a knot. The boy was afraid the dogs might choke. Lip-lip sometimes ran back toward the boy, rather than straight ahead, almost running over the other dogs.

Eventually, they learned to run next to one another without crossing the reins. Nor did any of them try to pass the dog in front. They stayed in two straight lines and pulled the sled as one.

This was as close to friendship as White Fang experienced with other dogs. When tied to the sled, they had to work as a team. There were still fights, but for the most part White Fang and the other dogs kept their distance. It was a truce of sorts.

White Fang enjoyed his work. He liked running through the snow, pulling against the leather straps across his chest. It was tiring and very hard work, but he had the energy for it. Also, he knew that it pleased his master when he performed well. It made White Fang proud to know that Gray Beaver was pleased.

White Fang took all his jobs seriously. He was also very dedicated when it came to guarding his master's possessions. No one would risk coming near Gray Beaver's tent or touching something that belonged to him. White Fang always seemed to be there. A deep, low growl met anyone who wandered in.

One afternoon, White Fang returned to the tent to see a strange man near the door flap. The wolf trotted around the other side of the tent and surprised the man from behind. White Fang walked toward the stranger, growling. The fur along his back was standing up and his scruff was raised.

"I—I, wait," the man said. He backed away with his hands raised to the wolf. "Gray Beaver sent me."

White Fang didn't understand the words this man spoke. He could smell his fear, though. He knew that this strange man was terrified. The wolf kept walking.

"W-w-white Fang," the man stuttered. "I'm picking up some tools." The man didn't see the rock behind him. He tripped and fell on his back. White Fang leaped toward him and took hold of his pant leg. The man started to scream.

"White Fang! Down!" It was Gray Beaver. He had returned to the tent just in time. He reached out to the man and helped him up.

The wolf went back to stand by the tent. Surely, his master would be angry that he had attacked a friend. But Gray Beaver started to laugh.

"So, Salmon Tongue," he said. "I see you couldn't get past my wolf."

The man brushed himself off. He was embarrassed and angry. "You sent me back here knowing White Fang would bite, didn't you?"

Gray Beaver shrugged. "Who's to say? White Fang is a good guard dog. You never know what he'll do."

Other men had joined them. They all listened with interest as Gray Beaver and Salmon Tongue argued.

"You knew what he would do."

"Maybe next time you should think twice about bragging. Your sled might be bigger and you might have more dogs," Gray Beaver said. "But you don't have White Fang." Gray Beaver smiled and crossed his arms over his chest.

Salmon Tongue was furious. He realized that his friend was jealous. Gray Beaver had let him walk into danger because he wanted to look more powerful. What if White Fang had bitten him on the leg, the arm, or the throat? Salmon Tongue was lucky that the wolf had only wanted to scare him.

"You're a dangerous man," he said. He pushed Gray Beaver back a step. "How dare you treat me—or anyone—that way!"

Salmon Tongue was just about to push him a second time when White Fang knocked the visitor to the ground. This time the wolf meant to do harm. His sharp teeth cut into the man's flesh as Gray Beaver pulled him off.

He pushed the wolf to a place of safety. White Fang watched the rest of the conversation while looking between Gray Beaver's legs. His master did not look angry. In fact, he looked quite happy.

"This is something everyone should think about," Gray Beaver told all the men. "No one gets past me—or my wolf."

The other men started to walk away. One

of them helped Salmon Tongue tie a bandage around his arm. He looked back at Gray Beaver and the wolf, shaking his head. Gray Beaver smiled.

But White Fang was not happy. The world as he saw it was fierce and brutal, a world without warmth, a world without caresses and affection. Gray Beaver liked that the wolf kept his distance from others, that he was hard and mean. It meant that Gray Beaver was more powerful and others were afraid of him.

White Fang had no real affection for his master. He did not love him. He knew his jobs and did them well. He lived his life hoping to avoid severe beatings and that was all.

After his mother left, White Fang was never touched in a kind or loving way. No one nuzzled him. No one made him feel safe. Soon he could barely remember her. He knew there was something missing from his life, something warm and loving, but he didn't have the power to name it. He lived his life in a constant state of stress. And because of this, he became hard and mean. He mistrusted both man and dog.

Lip-lip still terrorized him, but now White Fang fought back and often won. He fought any dog that came near. He stole food whenever he wanted. He might bite or snap at anyone—man, woman, or child—who crossed his path. He had no friends, but did not know what he was missing. It's hard to miss something that you have never had.

CHAPTER 11

Escape

⁓

White Fang became an expert fighter. He learned to jump unsuspecting dogs, flip them on their side, and attack their bellies. All of the dogs avoided him for this very reason. These fights were usually broken up quickly, with White Fang banished back to his tent. On those rare occasions when no men were around, the fights were more dangerous. The dogs fought until one gave up and a truce was called. As White Fang became meaner—and received more beatings from Gray

Beaver and no kindness from the other dogs—he was less able to let go. And then one day, a dog was killed.

It was a terrible and quick fight. White Fang was so strong and confident that it only took a few minutes. He trotted home afterward. He sat beside his master by the fire as if nothing strange had happened. White Fang didn't understand that he had done anything wrong. There was no one to guide him.

The owner of the other dog came to Gray Beaver and demanded payment for his loss. Gray Beaver wouldn't listen, though. "You can't change a wolf," he said. "And White Fang is my wolf."

That night by the fire, Gray Beaver gave White Fang an extra big piece of meat. "You're certainly a fighter," he said.

These were hard lessons for the wolf. He was

rewarded for his cruelty and fighting. His main focus in life was to please his master, and he thought fighting was the best way.

Gray Beaver was always quick with the beatings. It was difficult for White Fang to know right from wrong. The beatings often came at unexpected times. For instance, when he stole fish right from the hand of a small boy, Gray Beaver did not beat him. When the boy's father came to complain, threatening to hit White Fang, Gray Beaver protected him. However, when White Fang returned to his master's tent at the end of the day, he might be kicked without warning as he neared the fire. He never knew which it would be or why it happened. He learned to expect the worst.

The days were getting shorter. The tribe started to pack up camp and move south for winter. White Fang watched as Kloo-kooch tied up their belongings and Gray Beaver put them on a sled. The cub moved around camp and saw that others were doing the same. He understood that things were changing once again.

Most of the families had already left when White Fang went into the woods. He didn't go far, though—just far enough to be hidden. He could hear Gray Beaver calling him. It was very hard to disobey his master, but White Fang stayed put. After a while Gray Beaver stopped calling and the camp was silent. White Fang knew that he was once again alone in the Wild.

CHAPTER 12

Home Again

༄

Darkness was falling. For a while White Fang played among the trees, happy in his freedom. He ran quickly, jumping over rocks, searching for squirrels. He continued to play until all the daylight was gone. It was a clear night with many stars and a bright white moon. White Fang listened to the woods around him. It was very quiet, much quieter than life in the camp.

Then, quite suddenly, he became aware of loneliness. He sat down and listened to the silence. It frightened him. He suspected danger, but had no idea what to expect. It had been a long time since he was alone or in the Wild.

He ran back to the deserted camp. He was cold, hungry, and scared. He knew he had made a mistake by staying behind. He was too used to the comforts of man and to being protected by his master. He missed the warmth of the fire and the smell of Gray Beaver's pipe. Right about now, Kloo-kooch would be throwing him a fish supper. Mit'sah would be telling stories about his day.

He went to the place where Gray Beaver's tent had once stood. It still smelled of his master and family. He could see the pit that had once held their fire. The tent had left a round mark on the ground. He sat down, raised his head to the night sky, and started to howl. It was a long wolf-howl, full-throated and mournful. This was the first howl he had ever let out.

The coming dawn calmed him down, but he still longed to return to man. White Fang ran along the riverbank. He didn't know where his family had gone, or even if he was running in the right direction. The wolf worked on instinct. He spent the day running through the woods and back to the river, criss-crossing the land. He stopped to listen, hoping to hear the sound of far-off voices or other dogs. But there was only the sound of the wind. He sniffed the air and along the earth. He was trying to find some sign of the tribe, but it was hard to follow the scent over the frozen ground.

It was not until the moon was high in the sky again that he smelled something familiar. It was meat cooking on a fire. White Fang ran as fast as he could.

Gray Beaver, Kloo-kooch, and Mit'sah had stopped for the night. They planned to join the rest of the tribe across the river in the morning. White Fang sneaked into their camp.

He crept toward the fire. Kloo-kooch was turning meat over the flames while Mit'sah repaired some leather for the sled dogs. The family had to be ready for travel when the snow arrived. White Fang moved to Gray Beaver's side, expecting the usual beating. He lay quietly beside his master, accepting his fate.

Instead of giving him a hard slap, though, Gray Beaver chuckled. "Well, look who showed up," he said.

He waved his hand to Kloo-kooch, telling her to give the wolf some of the meat. "The biggest piece you have," he said. "Our wolf has come home."

White Fang lay at Gray Beaver's feet, gazing at the fire that warmed him, blinking and dozing. He knew that the morning would find him not in the cold, lonely forest, but safe with man. By coming back to the camp, White Fang had given up his life in the Wild. He was turning his back on his wolf heritage and choosing his master instead. He was now completely dependent on man, his food, and his fire.

CHAPTER 13

The Famine

❧

White Fang turned a year old. There was no one to wish him a happy birthday, though. In fact, there was no one who knew such an important date had arrived. He did not mind. That was not the kind of thing that concerned a wolf.

His life passed just as it always had. He kept his distance from the other dogs, except while working on the sled team. He spent a lot of time on his own running around the camp and through the woods. He got into more than a few fights. He was chased from more than a few tents for stealing.

And he received more than a few beatings from Gray Beaver.

As time went on, his master became meaner. Gray Beaver took advantage of the fact that people were afraid of White Fang. People in the camp kept their distance from him. Too many children received small bites. Too many women were frightened by his growls. Even Indians in other camps had heard about the wolf. Some even came to visit Gray Beaver so they could see White Fang firsthand. Gray Beaver held court as if he were a king on a throne. White Fang was his kingdom.

Another year passed in much the same way. White Fang turned two and, once again, no one noticed or cared. His days were still filled with fights, protecting Gray Beaver's property, or fending off blows from his master. This was White Fang's life and he never thought it should be different.

It was not until after his third birthday that

White Fang experienced true hunger again. Another famine hit the Northland and everyone suffered. There were no rabbits in any of the traps and far too few fish were caught. There was not even enough food to feed the members of the tribe. Many of the dogs, including White Fang, left for the Wild. They stood a better chance fending for themselves in the woods.

White Fang was better suited for this life than the others. The young wolf knew about life in the Wild. He quickly fell back into old patterns. He passed through familiar territory and visited old places. He found the cave where he and his mother used to live and the stream he had fallen into. He followed old trails and looked into nests and rabbit holes along the way. But there was little food to be found.

For weeks he survived on the occasional squirrel or small bird. One day he found a rabbit, but that did not add up to much against a hunger several weeks old. He could not remember the earlier famines. When he was a puppy, his mother and father found him food. They kept him alive when all his siblings passed away. Now that he was on his own, White Fang was becoming more desperate.

He tried going back to the Indian camp. He did not go in too far, though. He lurked around the outer edge, sniffing for scraps of food. There was very little to steal. Most of their traps were empty. White Fang understood that the Indians were also worried and desperate. He knew that they had little to offer. He looked for their rabbit snares. When life at the camp was bountiful, he would often raid these snares, grabbing fresh rabbit meat before one of the men found it. There was nothing now, though. White Fang returned to the woods, happy for whatever food he could find.

During his longest stretch of time without food, White Fang ran into Lip-lip. The older dog had also taken to the woods. It was an unexpected meeting. Walking in opposite directions along the base of a high cliff, they rounded a corner of rock and found themselves face-to-face.

The hair on White Fang's back rose. He bared his teeth and snarled. Then, before he even had a chance to think about it, White Fang jumped. It was over quickly. Lip-lip was not as skilled at life in the Wild as the wolf was. He had not been as successful at finding small bits of food, so he wasn't as strong. White Fang won this last fight and, at long last, ate a good meal.

Eventually the hunting became easier. White Fang found more food as he made his way through the woods. He ate his share and left the rest for others. This was one thing he remembered from his mother's first lessons. He must only use what he needed.

Without thinking too much about it, he started moving back toward the river. He

retraced his steps since living in the Wild. One day he found himself at the edge of the camp. It was a much happier place with children running and laughing and meat cooking on the fire. This time, White Fang walked right back in.

Gray Beaver welcomed him home with a nod. He didn't speak to the wolf or give him a fresh piece of meat. He continued repairing his fishing nets while White Fang sat beside him. They returned to their daily routine as though they had never been apart.

CHAPTER 14

Beauty Smith

∽

In the autumn, Gray Beaver and White Fang left the Indian camp. They traveled up the Mackenzie River and across the Rockies. Their trip lasted several months, as they stopped to camp and hunt along the way. It was a time of calm for White Fang, with no other dogs and only Gray Beaver nearby. He had hopes—if a wolf can, in fact, hope—that this was the start to a new life. Their time alone, however, was short lived.

White Fang and Gray Beaver arrived in Fort Yukon in the spring. This was the old Hudson's

Bay Company trading fort. It was the meeting place for anyone coming through that part of the North. There were many people, much food, and a great deal of excitement. Only a few people lived there fulltime. The population rose and fell with the arrival and departure of ships. It was a town full of people coming and going.

It was 1898, and thousands of gold-hunters were going up the Yukon to Dawson and the Klondike. They all wanted to make their fortune, but few did. Most people returned home as poor as when they left. The North could easily break one's spirit. Few people were strong enough to survive the weather, the loneliness, and the danger. The men and women who lived in Fort Yukon considered themselves a special breed. They laughed at newcomers. They bet on who would make it and who would fail. And when there was a windfall—when someone found gold and riches—money in the fort flowed freely.

Gray Beaver had heard about the gold rush, and he had come with several bales of furs and another bale of mittens and moccasins. He settled down to trade carefully and slowly. He, too, wanted to make his fortune, even if it took all summer and the next winter.

While Gray Beaver was busy working on his trades, White Fang took to the streets. People pointed at him, surprised to see a wolf. Thanks to his years with the dogs at camp, he was already an expert fighter. White Fang was soon the 'king' of Fort Yukon.

White Fang fought any dog that crossed his path and always won. These white man dogs were no match for a wolf. As Gray Beaver neither needed him to work nor cared if he wandered off, fighting filled most of his days. He quickly gained a reputation.

If he stopped in front of a store or office, someone rushed outside to shoo him away. They didn't want to lose customers because of the wolf. They knew no one would cross his path. A reverend at the chapel gave sermons against him. He claimed the wolf was a sign of the devil and must be stopped. People crossed the street to avoid him.

One person in particular noticed White Fang. His name was Beauty Smith, although he wasn't much of a beauty. His reputation was almost as bad as the wolf's. He had no friends and many enemies. He worked at many jobs and was usually quickly fired. He stole, lied, and gambled away what little money he had. Like so many others, Beauty had come to Fort Yukon in search of gold. Unlike most people, he decided to stay, but not because he loved the territory or challenges of the North. In reality, he didn't have any place else to go. The Northland was as good a place as any to stop.

Beauty was used to others picking on him and

calling him names. It had been that way for most of his life. Because of this, he was a bitter and jealous man. And as soon as he saw how powerful and strong White Fang was, Beauty Smith wanted the wolf for himself. He thought that he and the wolf would have much in common.

CHAPTER 15

A New Arrangement

∽

Beauty Smith wanted White Fang for himself and would stop at nothing to get him. He knew it would not be easy to get him away from his master. Even though Gray Beaver paid little attention to White Fang, he understood that the wolf was valuable. He was the strongest sled dog he had ever had. Therefore, Beauty needed a plan.

Gray Beaver was almost finished with Fort Yukon and would soon start his long trip home. Beauty sneaked into his camp when he knew Gray Beaver was in town. Using a heavy axe, he chopped Gray Beaver's sled in two. He broke the runners and smashed the body. There was no way to leave Fort Yukon during the winter without a sled.

His next step was to steal a new sled—an even better one—from the Hudson's Bay Company. He approached Gray Beaver offering to trade his "new" sled for White Fang. Gray Beaver thought carefully about it. It would be hard to let the wolf go, but he would need the sled to get home. He agreed to the trade.

Beauty Smith tied a piece of leather around White Fang's neck and pulled him away. The wolf did not want to go. He tugged at the rope and dragged his feet. But his master told him to go with this new man, so he stopped fighting. White Fang was worried, though. This new man made him uncomfortable.

Beauty was very quick to let White Fang know he was in charge. He surprised the wolf with a kick to the side of his head, knocking him sideways. White Fang did not have a moment to react before being thrown in a cage. Beauty locked the door and walked away.

This was yet another form of torture for White Fang. He had never been trapped before, or locked in such a small space. His instincts and nature demanded room, demanded that he roam. He paced back and forth as best he could. He was panicked and angry and could not understand how his master—Gray Beaver—had let this happen.

Beauty brought him food and water, but would not let him out of the cage. He poked at the wolf with a stick through the bars. White Fang growled and bit at the club and tried to jump at Beauty, but he couldn't pass between the bars. This went on for days. If he was let out, it was only so that Beauty could hit or kick him. Every day White Fang became angrier, more desperate for escape, and more dangerous.

At last there was a chance. Beauty opened the cage door just a little too wide and White Fang jumped through, knocking his cruel master down. The wolf did not stop for a moment. He ran back to Gray Beaver. There must have been a mistake. His master must be wondering what had happened to him.

Gray Beaver was surprised to see the wolf return. He was almost finished packing his new sled. Any later, and he would have been gone. White Fang ran to his side.

"What are you doing here?" Gray Beaver asked.

White Fang looked up at him. He did not know if he would receive praise or a beating. It did not matter, though. He knew this was where he belonged.

"You were sold,

fair and square," Gray Beaver said. "You have to go back."

Gray Beaver found some rope and tied it around White Fang's neck. "Let's go. You don't belong here any more."

White Fang followed his master because that was what he did. When they arrived at Beauty Smith's—and Gray Beaver handed him the rope—White Fang stopped fighting. He knew this was his fate. Although he could not understand these rules of man, he knew that he must obey.

Beauty beat him savagely, so much so that White Fang was sick. He threw the wolf back in his cage, locking it tight. Beauty was careful never to open the cage door so carelessly again. This was unnecessary, though, as White Fang never tried to escape again. Wasn't there someone who used to save him? Someone who would rush through the forest to rescue him from danger? These were only memories for White Fang. He could no longer recall his mother or her gentle touch. He accepted his fate. His fate was to be with Beauty Smith. His fate was to become meaner, angrier, and more spiteful than ever before.

CHAPTER 16

The Fighting Wolf

 ❧

It was time for White Fang to go back to work. This time, however, it was a whole new trade. Beauty Smith advertised him as "White Fang: The Fighting Wolf." Men paid money to watch White Fang fight other dogs, often to the death. They made bets on which dog would win. And it wasn't just dogs. White Fang was set against other wolves and even against a lynx.

White Fang learned to enjoy the fight. He certainly preferred fighting other animals to beatings from Beauty. He grew excited whenever men gathered around his cage. He knew this meant a fight was coming.

Beauty was a very cruel master. He enjoyed beating the wolf. Much like Gray Beaver, it made him feel powerful having such a strong animal under his control. But Beauty Smith was a coward. He did not show the wolf any mercy, protection, or justice. He never let him roam about and follow his wolf nature. He always kept him locked in the cage except when fighting.

One day a strange new dog was put into the fighting ring with the wolf. Many men were gathered—even more than usual—to see White Fang fight an English Bulldog. At first, White Fang thought his job would be easy. This dog was small and round. There would be no trouble knocking him over and taking hold. The bulldog seemed to be smiling. He wagged his tail at his master. His tongue was lolling out the side.

It was not an easy fight, though. It was one of

White Fang's hardest. Because the bulldog's legs were short and his body was wide, he was difficult to tip. And his jaws were incredibly strong. Once the bulldog had got hold of the fur around White Fang's neck, the wolf could not free himself. They were locked in a grip.

The men gathered around the cage cheered and egged them on. Bets were being placed back and forth, on one dog then the other. The longer the fight went on, the more money was being wagered. Beauty was very happy. He was making money and his dog was the center of attention.

White Fang did not notice two new men join the crowd. They were not cheering and betting like the others. One of them looked angry as he watched the dogs fight. He scanned the crowd.

White Fang was losing. He could not escape the grip of the bulldog. There was much shouting as the wolf started to go down. Beauty, realizing that he was about to lose a lot of money and that his road to fame and fortune was about to end, flew into a rage. He jumped into the ring and started kicking White Fang. There were hisses and some boos from the crowd, but that was it.

The newcomer—a young, clean-shaven man—turned on the men. "You cowards! You beasts!" he called.

He jumped into the ring and landed a smashing blow to Beauty's face. Beauty fell backward into the snow without knowing what hit him.

"Somebody help me get these dogs apart! Matt, get in here," the young man called to his friend.

"I'm right here, Weedon." Matt quickly followed his friend into the ring.

Beauty regained his feet and came back at the stranger. He did not get very far, though, as the young man once again knocked him to the ground. Beauty Smith decided that the snow was the safest place for him and made no further effort to get up.

CHAPTER 17

Weedon Scott

Weedon and Matt grabbed the bulldog and tried to pull him off. It was not easy. The young man very slowly pulled the bulldog's jaws open while Matt worked at freeing White Fang's mangled neck.

White Fang collapsed. His breathing was troubled. He did not have the strength to get up. He lay in the snow, dazed and unaware of the men talking above him.

"Matt, how much is a good sled dog worth?" Weedon asked.

Matt thought for a moment, then said, "Well, I'd say about three hundred dollars."

"And how much for one that's all chewed up like this one?" He pointed to White Fang.

"Half of that," was the dog-sledder's guess.

By this time, Beauty was on his feet and standing next to them. "I ain't selling," he said.

Weedon raised his fist toward Beauty.

"I've got my rights," Beauty whimpered.

"You gave up your rights to own that dog when you beat him and put him in the ring." Weedon looked Beauty straight in the eye. "Are you going to take the money?"

"All right," Beauty said quietly. "But I take the money under protest," he added. "The dog's a mint. I ain't goin' to be robbed."

Weedon turned his back on him and returned to help Matt, who was working over White Fang.

Some of the men were still standing outside the ring watching. Tim Keenan, the owner of the bulldog, asked, "Who is that man?"

"Weedon Scott," someone answered. "He's some kind of mining expert."

"Huh," Keenan sniffed. "And now I guess he's some kind of expert on wolves, too."

CHAPTER 18

Taming the Wolf

‸

"Well, Matt," Weedon said. "Do you think it's hopeless?"

He sat on the step of his cabin and stared at Matt. His friend responded with a shrug.

Together they looked at White Fang at the end of his stretched chain. The wolf was snarling, straining to get at the sled dogs.

"Is there any chance of taming him?" asked Weedon.

"Not sure," Matt said. "There might still be a lot of dog in him." Matt moved in as closely as he could. He examined White Fang—without touching him, of course—for a long time.

"Well, what is it?" Weedon asked. "Come on, spit it out. Why are you looking at him like that?"

"Wolf or no wolf," Matt said. "This dog has been trained." He pointed to marks along White Fang's fur where leather straps from a sled once lay.

"You're right. He was a sled dog before Beauty got a hold of him." Weedon was amazed. "So there's no reason he can't be trained again."

"Don't get too excited," Matt warned. "We've had him two weeks and he seems worse."

Weedon thought carefully for a moment. "We need to prove to him that he's not being punished. He needs to know that we won't hurt him."

"We could try turning him loose, I guess," Matt said.

Weedon thought about his friend's idea. It seemed risky but Matt was a careful man. "All right. Let him off his chain. We'll take a chance on him."

White Fang could hardly believe he was free. He had been with Beauty Smith for many months and in all that time he had never known freedom. He did not know what to make of it. There must be some sort of trick. He watched while the bigger man circled him and the little one went back into the cabin. White Fang stayed close to his corner, growling with his head down low.

"What he needs," said Weedon as he walked back outside, "is a little human kindness."

He threw a chunk of meat toward the hungry wolf. Before Matt had a chance to hold the other dogs back, one of their sled team jumped for the fresh meat. White Fang was on him in mere seconds. Matt and Weedon quickly pulled the wolf back while the dog ran off whimpering.

Matt quickly came to White Fang's defense. "Look, Weedon," he said. "That dog's had a rough go. You can't expect him to be as nice and shiny as an angel. You have to give him time."

"Don't worry," Weedon said. "I was being careless. I forgot the sled dogs might jump for the meat." He looked at White Fang. The wolf was confused and frightened, waiting for a beating or some abuse.

"All right, then," Weedon said. "We'll try something else."

He walked over to White Fang. Matt suggested that he take a club but Weedon shook his head. He spoke to the wolf in a gentle voice. White Fang waited for the beating. After all, he had attacked this man's property and hurt one of his dogs. This man was acting strangely, though. His voice was different. It was soft and low. This was something new, and one of the things White Fang understood was that "new" rarely meant better.

He bristled and showed his teeth, his body

shaking. This new man had no club. He didn't yell or kick or pull his chain. The man sat down very close to him. When a hand came out slowly toward him, White Fang offered a quick bite.

Weedon cried out sharply with surprise. He grabbed his torn hand and held it tightly.

"That's it," Matt said. He went into the shed for his rifle. "We can't take these chances. We have to put him down." Matt aimed the gun at White Fang.

The wolf reacted by jumping back into his corner, growling and hissing at Matt and the gun.

"No!" Weedon jumped up. "No, it's not his fault."

"Weedon, he bit you. He could do worse next time."

"Look at the intelligence of him," Weedon said. "He knows the meaning of firearms as well as you do. Watch. Put up your gun."

Matt put his gun down and White Fang immediately calmed down. He sat by the fence and continued to watch them.

"Pick it back up."

Matt did as he was told and White Fang reacted by lowering his head and growling, his fur bristling.

"Now, put it back down again."

White Fang's snarl disappeared once again.

Matt was amazed. "I agree with you completely. That dog's too smart to kill."

And so the retraining began. Every day, Weedon sat beside the wolf. He talked to White Fang in a kind, gentle voice. He wanted the wolf to get used to his voice, to understand kindness. Weedon Scott wanted White Fang to know that not everyone wanted to hurt him. He wanted him to learn trust.

"I'm still a bit worried about you sitting so close," Matt said at dinner. "I'm not saying you can't calm him down, but do you still think you can tame that wolf?"

"He's never known kindness," Weedon insisted. "He'll learn kindness by kind treatment."

Matt shook his head slowly. He knew what his friend said was true, but wild animals could be unpredictable. Especially one that had known so much abuse. "You're more optimistic than I am. I say if people can't be kind to each other, how do you expect a wolf to be?"

"That's just it," Weedon said. "People don't always treat each other with respect. You have to change the world one person—or one wolf—at a time."

Each morning before he set off to work, Weedon returned to White Fang. Every time he sat down, he moved a little closer. Eventually, he put his hand out. White Fang sniffed. Weedon moved his hand closer still and White Fang did not snap. Even though the wolf growled, he moved closer. Then he touched the fur along White Fang's back. The wolf's coat was matted and dirty. Weedon wondered if White Fang would ever trust him enough to let himself be cleaned. The wolf shied away slightly, but let Weedon gently press his hand into his back.

Matt stepped out of the cabin to empty a pan and saw his friend with the wolf. "Well, I'll be a monkey's uncle!" The sound of his voice broke the spell. White Fang jumped back snarling, teeth bared.

Weedon stood up and walked over to his friend. "I'm not sure what will happen now," he said. "But I think White Fang has finally learned some trust."

And the lessons did not stop there. Weedon kept up with his routine of sitting close to the wolf and talking low. White Fang slowly got used to people being near him. The wolf was still not fond of petting. He let Weedon touch him even though he growled the whole time. Weedon, however, was not fooled. He could hear the difference even if no one else could. It was not a harsh or mean growl. It had a different tone. It was a growl of comfort and growing love.

But about a month after White Fang came to live with Weedon and Matt, they saw a return of the vicious, angry wolf. One night after dinner the men were playing a game of cribbage when they heard a deep growl from the front porch. They opened the door to see the wolf, teeth bared, ready to spring into the darkness. Weedon and Matt looked into the darkness but could see nothing. Matt called, "Anybody there?" but no one answered.

Suddenly, the wolf leaped down the stairs and a man cried out in pain. Matt ran to grab a lantern while Weedon went for the wolf.

"Hold on, boy," he said. "Let's get a good look."

White Fang did not calm down at the sound of his master's voice, though. He continued to growl and snap and snarl. He tried to pull away from Weedon's arms and attack the whimpering man in front of him.

Matt returned with a lantern. He held the light up. "Aha," he said. "Well, that explains the wolf acting up."

Beauty Smith was lying in the snow, holding his leg where White Fang had bitten him. He continued to cry in pain although the wound did not look very deep.

"Get up, Smith," Weedon said. "What do you think you're doing out here?"

"I-I-I," he stuttered. White Fang continued to growl and Smith knew he was in trouble. "Just d-d-don't let go of the wolf, okay?"

"Why are you sneaking around our cabin in the dead of night, Smith?" Weedon asked. "I'm guessing it's not for a friendly visit."

"I came—I came to get my property," he whimpered. "My wolf." As soon as Smith looked at White Fang the wolf started to growl and snarl again.

"Do you really want me to let him go?" Weedon laughed. "Would you like it if I let you take White Fang home?"

The wolf struggled to free himself from his master's hold. His teeth were bared. His fur was standing straight up.

"N-n-no!" Smith cried. "No. Don't let go of him." He put his hands up in front of his face.

"White Fang will stay right where he is," Weedon said. "If you leave this instant."

"And remember," Matt said. "We won't hold him back if you try this again."

Smith mumbled something under his breath. He turned from the cabin and started limping back up the trail.

"Come on, boy," Weedon called the wolf back to the porch. "I think you should sleep inside tonight."

"Now, Weedon," Matt said. "You can't be worried that that coward Beauty Smith will try to take him again, are you?"

The young man led White Fang inside and cleared a space for him near the fireplace. "Yes, Beauty might try again. But I'm more worried we won't be around to stop the wolf next time."

Weedon sat down in a chair and lit his pipe. "You saw him out there. I thought he might kill the man." He looked over at the wolf that could be so gentle with him. White Fang was already sound asleep beside the fire.

CHAPTER 19

Abandoned

⌒♈

White Fang's life with his new master went along smoothly. There were no beatings, plenty of food, and many kind words. Still, it took White Fang a long time to adjust. The wolf continued to bare his fangs at other dogs and was still nervous about hands coming too close. His new master never lost patience, though, and White Fang slowly learned to accept this new way. Although he did not wag his tail or whine with excitement when Weedon approached, he showed his affection in other ways. Even though it was Matt who fed him, White Fang was devoted only to Weedon.

Matt put White Fang back to work on the sleds. He liked pulling the sled and happily did his best. Every day the team went out to pick up supplies or inspect the area. This was much easier work than with Gray Beaver. They covered less distance and the loads were lighter. He worked well with the other dogs, but still kept his distance. There were no fights this time. Matt would not allow it. He pulled apart any animals who tried.

One morning his master went off on his own sled. Weedon often spent the days working elsewhere so White Fang was not worried. This time, though, he did not return in the evening and was still gone the next morning. The other man did not seem bothered. Matt worked the dogs as usual, taking them into town to pick up supplies. White Fang, however, was growing worried.

When Weedon was still gone after several

days, he refused to eat. He sat on the porch of their cabin whimpering. He pawed at the front door, hoping his master would open it. But his master was gone. White Fang started to feel that familiar sense of mistrust. His master had disappeared. The wolf suddenly felt forgotten.

Matt was worried about the wolf's health so he brought him inside. He wrote a letter to Weedon telling him about White Fang.

"The wolf won't work. He won't eat. He wants to know where you've gone."

White Fang lay on the floor near the stove, without interest in food or Matt. The man tried talking gently to him, but it did not matter. It was Weedon that he wanted.

Late one night, Matt was startled by a low whine coming from White Fang. He was on his feet at last, his ears cocked toward the door. A moment later, there were footsteps on the porch. The door opened and Weedon stood before them.

"Where's the wolf?" he asked.

White Fang was standing near the stove. He did not rush forward like other dogs. He stood, watching and waiting.

"By George!" said Matt. "Look at him wag his tail."

Weedon stepped quickly across the room and knelt before his wolf. He rubbed his hands through his fur while White Fang sounded his crooning growl.

And then, quite suddenly, White Fang thrust his head forward. He pushed his way in between his master's arm and body. Weedon wrapped his arms tightly around him while his wolf continued to nudge and snuggle.

White Fang was changing. He was learning to do things that other dogs took for granted: wagging his tail, greeting his master at the door, and snuggling in close. He was learning how to love.

CHAPTER 20

On to California

It was in the air. White Fang sensed something was coming. Something that he would not like. His master was acting strangely. Things around the cabin were being moved and put into boxes and trunks. White Fang started to suspect that Weedon was going to leave again.

"Listen to that, would you," Matt said. A low, very sad whine was coming through the door from the front porch.

"What am I supposed to do?" Weedon asked. "I can't take a wolf to California."

"I'm not arguing with you. I'm just saying, I think that wolf's on to you." Matt went back to packing some of his friend's things.

Weedon listened to his wolf crying. This was a terrible thing, but what else could he do? It would not be fair to take him south. It was not his home.

"All right," Matt said. "We're all set. Let's get you to that boat." He finished closing the last suitcase.

The two men had already worked out a plan. As Matt put together the last few things to carry outside, Weedon called White Fang inside.

"I'm hitting the trail, old friend," he said. There were tears in Weedon's eyes. He knew it would be hard saying goodbye, but had not expected to feel this sad. "You can't follow me this time. Now give me a growl—the last, good, goodbye growl." He snuggled with White Fang for the last time.

Weedon stood up quickly, walked to the door, and shut it before White Fang knew what was happening. The young man did not even look back—he could not look back. It was too hard.

He and Matt walked up the trail to catch the boat, listening to White Fang's howls. The wolf was trapped in the cabin and desperately trying to get out. The sound of him scraping at the front door followed them up the trail.

At the boat, Matt helped Weedon bring his bags on board. "You'll take good care of him, won't you," he said. "And you'll write and let me know how he's doing."

"Of course," Matt answered. "I just hope he forgives me when I get back to the cabin."

There was some commotion on board. People near them started to whisper and point. Matt's jaw dropped in amazement. Sitting several feet away from them was White Fang.

"Did you lock the front door?" Matt asked. He was very confused.

Weedon nodded.

White Fang walked carefully over to his master and sat at his feet. Weedon checked the wolf and noticed fresh cuts along his muzzle and matted fur.

"We forgot one thing," he said in amazement. "We forgot the window." He looked up at Matt. "He jumped through the window to follow us."

"Well, I'll be," Matt shook his head.

Weedon stood up with a smile on his face. "Don't worry about writing to me about the wolf, Matt. I'll write to you instead."

"What? Weedon, you can't be serious…"

"I'm very serious," he turned and bent back over the wolf, rubbing his belly and scratching behind his ears. "White Fang is coming home with me."

CHAPTER 21

Weedon's Home

∽

The boat carrying Weedon Scott and White Fang arrived in San Francisco. They stepped off the boat onto a crowded busy dock. White Fang had never known a world like this before. The city was too much for the wolf. There were concrete roads, tall buildings, cars, and so many people everywhere. There were too many smells, too many people, too much to take in. He was afraid of all the noise. There were so many humans, and so many human legs to work his way past. He had lost his sense of direction and did not know which way to turn. He was terrified that he might lose sight of his master. He felt completely dependent on the young man. He followed closely at his heels. Even other dogs and children did not distract him.

Thankfully, they did not stay long in the city. White Fang would only remember it as a bad dream. Weedon took him to the railway station and put him into a baggage-car train. When the steel doors of the car slammed shut and Weedon was not with him, White Fang feared he had lost his master. He sat near Weedon's bags, keeping careful watch. Even if he did lose his master, he would make sure that Weedon's things were well protected. Somehow, White Fang knew that his master would come back looking for him.

It was only an hour later when the steel doors opened again and White Fang emerged from the car. He was amazed. The city was gone. He was back in more familiar territory—although not quite home. All the sights and sounds of city life were gone. They were in a country that was very green with many tall trees. There were no tall trees in the North. White Fang had never seen rolling hills and green forests like these. California was a very different place.

A carriage was waiting for them and two people approached Weedon. White Fang watched with horror as these people wrapped their arms around his master. They squeezed him one at a time. His master was under attack! Weedon rushed to reassure White Fang, who had become a snarling, raging demon.

"It's all right, mother," he said, while holding White Fang tightly. "He thought you were trying to hurt me. Don't worry. He'll learn soon enough."

"In the meantime," she said. "I'll learn to hug my son when the wolf is not around." She laughed, but was clearly shaken.

Weedon made White Fang sit quietly and hugged his mother again. When the wolf started to growl again, Weedon warned, "Down! Down!" Eventually, White Fang learned to sit quietly while his master hugged his parents. He understood that there was no danger.

The bags were loaded into the carriage and they set off down the road, with White Fang running behind. The wolf was happy to run. The long boat ride had been very difficult for him. He was not used to such small spaces where he could not run around or explore his surroundings. Now that he was free again, White Fang ran with all his might. This new land smelled wonderful. There were so many new sights and sounds. The wolf wanted to run through the woods to see what he might find, but did not want to lose sight of his master. After fifteen minutes, the carriage pulled into a driveway and White Fang followed.

More people ran out from the house to greet them, including two young children. This worried White Fang and he kept his distance. The children in the Indian village had often teased or hurt him. The children in Fort Yukon threw sticks and stones at him. Luckily, these two were more interested in the return of their father and didn't pay much attention to the wolf.

More troubling still were the two farm dogs that met White Fang with snarls and barks. The hound bit at his heels while White Fang ran after the carriage. The other—a female collie—blocked his way at every turn. She would not let him get too close to the family. He was kept at a distance from his master. White Fang was more panicked than angry. He could see his master twenty feet away, but could not reach him. He tried going left. He tried going right. It did not matter. The collie was always right there.

Weedon looked over his shoulder to see White Fang's struggle.

"Here, Collie," he called. "Stop that!" The collie stopped in her tracks and White Fang ran up to Weedon.

"Well, he's certainly attached to you," said Judge Scott, Weedon's father. "I'm impressed."

"He learns quickly," Weedon said while patting White Fang's head. "But we should be careful for the first bit. He trusts me but hasn't had much experience with other people. Not with kind people, at least."

"Let's go inside. Supper must be ready," Judge Scott said. "We'll bring in the collie and leave White Fang and the hound to work it out themselves." The family started to walk toward the house. White Fang watched Weedon carefully.

Weedon chuckled. "I think White Fang should stay with us. Otherwise we might not have a hound dog to deal with later."

His father looked at the wolf and remembered his growls at the train station. White Fang stood close to Weedon's side. He was standing guard by his master. "Perhaps you're right, son. Perhaps you're right."

CHAPTER 22

The Chicken Coop

His life with Gray Beaver had taught White Fang that he should protect his master's property. So he was very surprised when Weedon punished him for attacking an intruder. He only gave the man a small bite in the hand, but Weedon was furious. Even the collie barked and snapped at him.

White Fang knew nothing about grooms or farm hands. When he saw a strange man walk into the barn and take something, he thought he was a thief. The poor boy—who had only come to do his job and rake out the barn—let out a terrified cry when White Fang ran at him.

The collie was first on the scene. She bit at the wolf's heels. She barked and nipped at the wolf until he left the groom alone. Thankfully, White Fang had only bitten his arm as a warning. There was no damage done, except for the fact that the groom was too scared to come back to the Scotts' farm.

Life on the farm was like nothing White Fang had ever experienced. For the first while he expected something terrible—a famine, a beating, or an attack of some kind. Nothing happened, though. He was allowed to run about the property and everyone was kind. It was never easy with the other dogs—especially the collie—but there were never serious fights. They watched each other closely, but kept their distance.

The children were another matter. His experiences in the Indian camp or Fort Yukon had not been good. Those children had taunted and teased, and White Fang had learned to mistrust them. Weedon's children, though, were gentler. Also, the wolf knew that they belonged to his master, so he could do them no harm. Eventually, he learned to tolerate their hands on his fur and even learned to like their soft words.

White Fang did not understand that some people kept animals on a farm. When he saw a chicken coop—full of so many chickens—he did not realize they were not for him. As soon as he found the door open, White Fang ran in and killed two of the chickens. Weedon's parents, however, did not take it so lightly.

"Your wolf broke into the chicken coop!" Mrs. Scott was furious. She walked out onto the front porch to confront her son.

Weedon apologized to his mother. He said it would never happen again as he set off to find White Fang.

"Never again!" His father laughed. "Are you

trying to tell me you can stop a wolf—a wild animal—from hunting our chickens?"

"I'm saying just that," Weedon challenged. "You don't believe me?"

"Sorry, son." His father shook his head. "But a wolf is a wolf."

"Then we'll have to prove you wrong." Weedon started to walk away, but stopped. "Let's have a friendly bet. After I teach White Fang the error of his ways, I'll bet he can sit in the chicken coop for an entire afternoon without killing a single bird."

His father laughed. "That, my dear boy, is the easiest bet I've ever made."

"And for every ten minutes he is in the coop and doesn't kill a bird," Weedon added. "You will have to say, 'White Fang, you are smarter than I thought.'"

Judge Scott agreed to the terms.

Weedon could not punish White Fang just yet.

He had to catch him in the act. When he found the wolf with a dead bird, he talked harshly, his voice angry and severe. He held White Fang's nose down to the slain hens and cuffed him soundly. His master never hit him, so White Fang knew this was serious.

So, when he found himself inside the coop for many hours, he waited calmly for his release. He knew that he could not touch the chickens. He knew they were off-limits. The part that confused him was sitting on the front porch afterward. The old man sat beside him, repeating the same words over and over. Everyone around him was laughing. White Fang knew that this laughter was not directed at him. It was not mean-spirited or cruel. At long last, he was learning to like the sound of laughter. And White Fang never raided a chicken roost again.

CHAPTER 23

Weedon Gets Injured

∽

Whenever Weedon went on errands or into town, White Fang went with him. His master rode on his horse or in a carriage while White Fang followed behind.

The wolf had left his old ways behind. He had changed a lot since his days of roaming the streets of Fort Yukon. Now that he was with Weedon, he knew that he could not attack other dogs. Fighting was not allowed.

It was hard when other dogs in town bothered White Fang. He tried to ignore them, but they would not go away. They bit at his heels and tried to trip him up. Every once in a while, the wolf turned and snarled at them. It did not help, though. Every time Weedon went to town, White Fang was picked on.

This went on for weeks before Weedon noticed. As White Fang ran after his carriage—and away from the dogs—the carriage stopped. Weedon stepped down and told the wolf that it was okay.

"Go on, boy," Weedon said. "You can take after them."

White Fang looked at him, confused. Go after the dogs?

"It's all right. You can go."

White Fang turned around and went off after the dogs. He chased them down the street and around the corner. It was the last time he was bothered by the dogs.

And that's how it was with Weedon Scott. He

was not quick to anger, but would always quietly come to White Fang's defense. When children outside his office were throwing sticks and rocks at the wolf, Weedon stopped it. After one firm lecture they never came back.

White Fang also followed his master on horseback when Weedon went for a ride through the countryside. They could run for hours together. The wolf had plenty of time to run through the trees and chase squirrels. It reminded him of hunting with his mother in the Wild. Those were the days before Beauty Smith, before Gray Beaver. Although he didn't have the words to describe his feelings, White Fang knew that he was happy.

One day, though, disaster struck. Weedon's horse lost its footing and tumbled. Weedon was thrown and his horse rolled over on him. Weedon's leg was broken and he couldn't get up.

White Fang ran to his master. He sniffed and whimpered, trying to encourage him to get up.

"Home!" Weedon commanded. "Go home!"

It took a few moments for the wolf to understand. He ran back toward the house, but returned to his master, amazed to see him in the same spot. "It's all right," Weedon said more gently. "Go back home now."

White Fang ran all the way at top speed.

The Scott family was sitting on the porch. White Fang ran up the stairs so quickly that he almost knocked Weedon's wife over.

"My word!" she exclaimed. "What on earth could be wrong with him?"

White Fang ran off the porch then back on. He was so wild that he scared the children.

"I must confess," Weedon's mother said. "He makes me nervous around the children."

White Fang started to growl.

"A wolf is a wolf," said Judge Scott. "There is no trusting one." He went back to reading his paper.

White Fang moved from one person to the next. He nudged them, then ran back toward the trail.

Weedon's wife stood up. "But if White Fang's back, where is Weedon? White Fang wouldn't leave him unless something was wrong."

There were all on their feet now. For the second and last time in his life, White Fang barked and was understood.

The family found Weedon and brought him home. After that, White Fang held a special place in everyone's heart. Even the collie was nicer to him. She let him run in the woods with her or around the yard, just as the red dog had run with One Eye years before. No one doubted now that a wolf could change.

CHAPTER 24

Jim Hall's Revenge

∽

White Fang's adventures were not over quite yet. There was one more surprise in store for him.

A prisoner had escaped from a nearby jail. Jim Hall was a violent and dangerous man. Judge Scott had sentenced Hall to fifty years in jail for his many crimes and offenses. Hall swore revenge.

When news of his escape reached the Scott family, they were all worried. Everyone except the judge. He did not think Hall would bother with him.

"The police will catch him soon enough," he said. "There's no need to worry."

Weedon's wife thought the family needed more protection. It was good to keep everyone from worrying, but she took no chances. Each night after everyone was in bed, she let White Fang in. The wolf slept in the front hall, guarding the house. Each morning she let him back out before anyone else was up.

On one such night, White Fang smelled something strange. There was something dangerous in the house. He walked softly to the staircase and saw a man.

The stranger moved quietly around the corner. He stayed very close to the wall, making no sound as he walked. Just as the man lifted a foot to walk up the stairs, White Fang attacked.

The man cried out. White Fang's teeth sank into his leg. The wolf pulled him off the stairs and on to the floor. The hall was dark and the man could not see his attacker. They continued to roll on the carpet together. A revolver was fired three times. The fight was over.

The whole house woke up and ran to the front hall. Weedon turned on the lights. There was Jim Hall, lying on the rug. He was dead. Beside him lay White Fang, breathing very slowly.

Weedon went to his side. "White Fang!"

The wolf gave a soft growl, trying to look up at his master, but he had no strength.

"I'm right here," he said. Weedon stroked the wolf's head. "Don't worry. We'll get you help."

The judge rode into town to notify the police and to bring back a surgeon for White Fang. As dawn broke, the family waited nervously for a report.

"There are three broken ribs, a broken hind leg, and three bullet holes," the doctor said. "I'm sorry to say that this will be difficult."

"Spare no expense," the judge said. "Treat this

wolf as you would any hero. We owe him our lives." The surgeon said that he understood and went to work on the wolf.

The entire Scott family sat quietly in the living room. Weedon's wife wept softly, saying a prayer that White Fang's life would be saved. No one wanted to think what might have happened without their wolf. No one wanted to think what life might be like if their wolf did not make it.

Weedon sat by the window on his own. He cried quietly to himself. "Please, boy" he whispered. "You can do it. Don't let me down."

After what felt like hours, the surgeon returned. Thankfully, he had good news to report.

"Your wolf made it through the operation," he said.

Weedon's children clapped and the judge slapped him on the back. "Thank goodness, Doctor," he said. "We couldn't be happier."

"Can I go and see him?" Weedon asked.

"He's still asleep, but you can check in if you'd like," the doctor answered. "But you should know that it will be a long recovery period. There were three bullets in him and it will take a long time to heal. He's going to be in a cast for quite some time, too."

Weedon hugged the doctor. "He's going to be just fine," the young man said. "I can feel it."

He went to see his wolf. The dining room had been turned into a temporary operating room. White Fang was lying on his side on the table. His ribcage was wrapped in bandages and there was a cast on his leg. He did not look sick. He looked like he was sleeping very soundly.

"So what do you say, old boy," Weedon whispered. "Let's make this our last adventure. How about we live a nice quiet life after this?"

CHAPTER 25

A Family of His Own

White Fang was never alone. When he woke up from his operation, Weedon was right there talking to him. At first he was worried and confused. The last thing he remembered was the strange man in the hallway. He tried to get up so he could check that the house was safe. His legs would not work, though. He could not walk around.

"Stay where you are," his master said. "Everything is fine."

His master's voice was soft and calm. It was

just like the first time he spoke to the wolf—in the Northland, before he was tamed. White Fang thought that the danger must be gone since his master did not sound angry or nervous. So the wolf went back to sleep. He could finally get a good rest without worry.

Weedon and his family took very good care of White Fang. Weedon's wife fed him by hand. The children brought him blankets and slowly stroked his head. Judge Scott and his wife checked on him every chance they got. And Weedon rarely left his side.

The day finally came when the doctor removed the cast. Poor White Fang was still very weak, but could at last move around. At first he could only walk from one room to the other. He was so tired that he had to lie down again. Eventually he could walk farther, even venturing outside.

"Today will be a big day for you," Weedon said.

He scratched behind White Fang's ears. The wolf nuzzled into his arm and softly growled.

"We're going out to the barn. I want you to meet someone."

The whole family was very excited. They all walked with White Fang across the back lawn. It took him a long time, but he finally made it.

The collie was lying inside the barn on a straw bed. Six tiny puppies were beside her. Two of them were all gray and looked just like their father. She growled when the family entered the barn, warning them all not to hurt her babies.

White Fang walked over to his new family. He lay down in the straw, ignoring the collie's growls. Weedon and his family crouched near the doorway, watching the new puppies and parents. One of the puppies sprawled in front of White Fang. He cocked his ears and looked at it. Then their noses touched. He felt the warm little tongue of the

puppy on his muzzle. White Fang's tongue went out and he licked the puppy's face.

Hand-clapping and happy shouts came from the Scott family. White Fang was surprised and looked strangely at them.

The other puppies came crawling toward White Fang. At first the collie was upset, but she did not stop them. She knew White Fang would not hurt them. They started to climb over their father.

At first, White Fang felt strange about all the attention and worried that the puppies would hurt his side. This passed away as the puppies' antics and playing continued. He lay dozing in the sun with his eyes half-shut.

White Fang could not express what he was feeling. His life before Weedon Scott—a life of beatings, hardships, and fighting—was a distant memory. The rest of his days were spent with the Scotts on their farm. There were no more disasters and no big adventures. He was at long last safe and warm. Even if he did not know the word for it, White Fang felt love.

What Do *You* Think?
Questions for Discussion

⌒

Have you ever been around a toddler who keeps asking the question "Why?" Does your teacher call on you in class with questions from your homework? Do your parents ask you questions about your day at the dinner table? We are always surrounded by questions that need a specific response. But is it possible to have a question with no right answer?

The following questions are about the book you just read. But this is not a quiz. They are designed to help you look at the people, places, and events in the story from different angles. These questions do not have specific answers. Instead, they might help you think of the story in a completely new way.

Think carefully about each question and enjoy discovering more about this classic story.

1. *White Fang* is considered by many to be a story about the "survival of the fittest." What do you think this means?

2. How does the author make White Fang seem more like a human than an animal? Can you think of any other stories you've read where this occurs?

3. The red dog is a very protective mother. Does she act like any parents you know?

4. The red dog teaches White Fang that "even enemies must have respect for one another." What do you think this means? Do you agree?

5. At the end of chapter nine, White Fang falls asleep wondering what the new day will bring. Do

you think he would be hopeful or nervous about tomorrow? How do you feel about each new day?

6. Why does White Fang choose to return to Gray Beaver after he runs away? What would you have done in his situation?

7. The author says that it is hard to be fair and honest when no one treats you that way. Have you ever been in a situation like this?

8. Beauty Smith's name seems unusual. Why do you think this is? Have you ever met anyone whose name didn't seem to match his or her personality?

9. How does the way Gray Beaver treats White Fang differ from the way Weedon Scott treats him? Do you know anyone like either of these characters?

10. How does White Fang change from the beginning to the end of the book?

A Note to Parents and Educators

by Arthur Pober, EdD

⌒

First impressions are important.

Whether we are meeting new people, going to new places, or picking up a book unknown to us, first impressions count for a lot. They can lead to warm, lasting memories or can make us shy away from any future encounters.

Can you recall your own first impressions and earliest memories of reading the classics?

Do you remember wading through pages and pages of text to prepare for an exam? Or were you the child who hid under the blanket to read with a flashlight, joining forces with Robin Hood to save Maid Marian? Do you remember only how long it took you to read a lengthy novel such as *Little Women*? Or did you become best friends with the March sisters?

Even for a gifted young reader, getting through long chapters with dense language can easily become overwhelming and can obscure the richness of the story and its characters. Reading an abridged, newly crafted version of a classic novel can be the gentle introduction a child needs to explore the characters and story line without the frustration of difficult vocabulary and complex themes.

Reading an abridged version of a classic novel gives the young reader a sense of independence and the satisfaction of finishing a "grown-up" book. And when a child is engaged with and inspired by a classic story, the tone is set for further exploration of the story's themes, characters, history, and details. As a child's reading skills advance, the desire to tackle the original, unabridged version of the story will naturally emerge.

If made accessible to young readers, these stories can become invaluable tools for understanding themselves in the context of their families and social environments. This is why the *Classic Starts* series includes questions that stimulate discussion regarding the impact and social relevance of the characters and stories today. These questions can foster lively conversations between children and their parents or teachers. When we look at the issues, values, and standards of past times in terms of how we live now, we can appreciate literature's classic tales in a very personal and engaging way.

Share your love of reading the classics with a young child, and introduce an imaginary world real enough to last a lifetime.

Dr. Arthur Pober, EdD

Dr. Arthur Pober has spent more than twenty years in the fields of early-childhood and gifted education. He is the former principal of one of the world's oldest laboratory schools for gifted youngsters, Hunter College Elementary School, and former Director of Magnet Schools for the Gifted and Talented for more than 25,000 youngsters in New York City.

Dr. Pober is a recognized authority in the areas of media and child protection and is currently the U.S. representative to the European Institute for the Media and European Advertising Standards Alliance.

Explore these wonderful stories in our
Classic Starts™ audio library.

20,000 Leagues Under the Sea

The Adventures of Huckleberry Finn

The Adventures of Tom Sawyer

Black Beauty

A Little Princess

Little Women

The Secret Garden

The Swiss Family Robinson

Treasure Island

White Fang